OXFORD

GCSE N

Foundation PLUS

Homework

Claire Turpin Sidney Stringer School, Coventry

About this book

This book has been written to provide extra exercises for the topics covered within the Foundation Plus Student Book. There are four exercises for each Student Book unit: Homework 1 reviews previous topics, Homework 2 covers unit lessons 1 and 2, Homework 3 covers unit lessons 3 and 4 and Homework 4 covers unit lesson 5 as well as reviewing the rest of the unit with exam-style questions.

Contents

OXFORD
UNIVERSITY PRESS

OXFORD
UNIVERSITY PRESS

Great Clarendon Street, Oxford OX2 6DP

Oxford University Press is a department of the University of Oxford.
It furthers the University's objective of excellence in research, scholarship,
and education by publishing worldwide in

Oxford New York

Auckland Cape Town Dar es Salaam Hong Kong Karachi
Kuala Lumpur Madrid Melbourne Mexico City Nairobi
New Delhi Shanghai Taipei Toronto

With offices in

Argentina Austria Brazil Chile Czech Republic France Greece
Guatemala Hungary Italy Japan South Korea Poland Portugal
Singapore Switzerland Thailand Turkey Ukraine Vietnam

Oxford is a registered trade mark of Oxford University Press
in the UK and in certain other countries

British Library Cataloguing in Publication Data

Data available

ISBN 0 19 915083-4

ISBN 978 0 19 915083-0

10 9 8 7 6 5 4 3 2

Typeset by MCS Publishing Services Ltd., Salisbury, Wiltshire

Printed in Great Britain by Ashford Colour Press Ltd., Gosport

Front cover photo: Jupiter Images/Creatas

1 Look at these number cards.

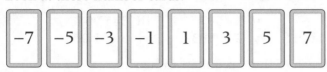

-7 -5 -3 -1 1 3 5 7

a Choose two cards that add to 2.
b Choose two cards that add to −8.
c Choose any four cards that add to make 0.
d What is the total of adding all eight cards?

2 a Here are three number cards.

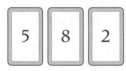

5 8 2

Show that the mean of these numbers is 5.

b The mean of three numbers is 4.
One of these numbers is 3.
i What could the other numbers be?
ii What else could the numbers be?
Use different numbers from your answer to part **i**.

3 When n is 6, work out the value of $2(n + 3)$.

4 The diagram shows four identical white rectangles
(8 cm by 3 cm) around a shaded square.
What is the area of the square?

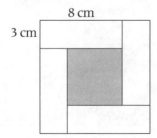

8 cm

3 cm

1

1 a Write each of these numbers in words.

  i   567   **ii** 11 567   **iii** 345 004
  vi 120 001   **v**   3450.03   **vi** 3 001 003

  b Write each of these numbers in figures.

  i   One hundred thousand
  ii Thirty two thousand and four
  iii One million and twenty six
  iv Twenty two thousand and twenty point four
  v   One hundred thousand point zero five.

2 Use the information given to work out each of these
  calculations without using a calculator.

  a $34 \times 45 = 1530$ What is 3.4×45?
  b $94 \times 49 = 4606$ What is 94×4.9?
  c $28 \times 35 = 980$ What is 2.8×3.5?
  d $78 \times 27 = 2106$ What is 0.78×27?
  e $56 \times 29 = 1624$ What is 5600×29?

3 Write the number that each of the arrows is pointing to.

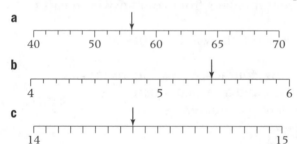

a

40   50   60   65   70

b

4   5   6

c

14   15

4 Here is the Fowey–St Austell
  bus timetable.
  a How long does the 11.22 bus
    from Tywardreath take to get
    to St Austell?
  b Between which two towns
    does the journey take the longest?

Fowey	11.10	11.40
Tywardreath	11.22	11.52
Par	11.29	11.59
St Blazey	11.36	12.06
St Austell	11.58	12.28

1 Write these numbers in order starting with the smallest.

   a −4, 9, 0, −6, 12, −15
   b −1, 1, 5, −9, 3, 10
   c 12, 3, −2, 3, 0, −4
   d −5, 10, −35, 13, 3, 20
   e 0, −10, 9, 3, −5, −20
   f −100, 30, 0, −29, 39, 12

2 Find the number that lies exactly halfway between these pairs of numbers.

   a −3 and 3   **b** −5 and 3   **c** −10 and −6
   d −12 and 10   **e** −3 and 5   **f** −4.5 and 0.5

3 Calculate these.

   a 4 − 5   **b** −3 + 4   **c** −4 + −5
   d 15 − 18   **e** 14 − −4   **f** −4 − −3
   g −3 + 15   **h** −10 − 3   **i** 14 + −14
   j −8 − −3   **k** −7 + −4   **l** 6 + −6
   m −4 × 5   **n** 9 × −3   **o** −11 × 0
   p −5 × −4   **q** 10 × −5   **r** −4 × −4
   s 5 × −3   **t** −6 × −6   **u** −96 ÷ 12
   v −12 × −12   **w** −99 ÷ 3   **x** −24 × 8

4 Choose a number card to make each of these calculations correct.

$$\boxed{-4}\ \boxed{-2}\ \boxed{2}\ \boxed{5}\ \boxed{-5}\ \boxed{4}$$

   a $2 \times \boxed{} = -4$ **b** $4 \div \boxed{} = -2$

   c $\boxed{} \times 5 = 25$ **d** $\boxed{} \div -5 = 1$

   e $-2 \div \boxed{} = \frac{1}{2}$ **f** $\boxed{} \times -4 = 8$

   g $\boxed{} \div 2 = -2$ **h** $-5 \times \boxed{} = -20$

1 a Use the information that

$17 \times 16 = 272$

to write the value of

i 1.7×1.6
ii $27.2 \div 1600$

b Use the information that

$17 \times 16 = 272$

to find the least common multiple (LCM)
of 17 and 32.

2 a Find the highest common factor (HCF) of 108 and 36

b Find the highest common factor (HCF) of 72 and 96.

3 If $3.46 \times 457 = 1581.22$
write the answer to

a 0.346×4570
b 34.6×0.457

4 Jordan wrote the temperatures at different times on
1st February 2005.

a What was

i the highest
temperature
ii the lowest
temperature?

Time	Temperature in °C
Midnight	−7
5 am	−10
11 am	1
4 pm	6
9 pm	−2

b Work out the difference in the temperature between

i midnight and 5 am
ii 5 am and 4 pm.

At 11 pm the temperature has fallen by 4 °C from its
value at 9 pm.

c Work out the temperature at 11 pm.

1 Write each of these numbers in figures.

  a Three thousand and four
  b Forty five thousand and six
  c Ninety thousand and ten
  d Nine million, two thousand and four hundred.

2 Write each of these numbers in words.

  a 7500   **b** 217 800
  c 95 012   **d** 707 007
  e 990 909   **f** 7 048 003

3 Use the information given to work out each of these calculations without using a calculator.

  a $37 \times 43 = 1591$ What is 37×4.3?
  b $87 \times 69 = 6003$ What is 8.7×6.9?
  c $64 \times 61 = 3904$ What is 6.4×61?
  d $58 \times 83 = 4814$ What is 0.58×83?
  e $39 \times 59 = 2301$ What is 3900×59?

4 Calculate each of these

a $7 - 11$	**b** $-6 + 7$	**c** $-6 + -7$
d $12 - 24$	**e** $14 - -7$	**f** $-6 - -11$
g $-8 + 35$	**h** $-19 - 8$	**i** -4×12
j 7×-7	**k** -6×0	**l** -12×-3
m 14×-7	**n** -6×-9	**o** 7×-11
p -9×-6	**q** -3×2	**r** -13×-6

5 In each of these expressions $a = -4$, $b = 3$ and $c = -6$. Calculate the value of these expressions.

a $b + 5$	**b** $2b - 7$	**c** $a - b$
d $b + 3c$	**e** $a + 2b + c$	**f** $a + b - 3c$
g $4c - b - a$	**h** $c - 3a + b$	**i** $a \times b$
j $b \times c$	**k** $ab + c$	**l** $3bc - a$

S1 HW2 Measures, perimeter and area

1 Convert these measurements to the units given.

    a 30 mm = ___ cm   **b** 300 cm = ___ m

    c 3 kg = ___ g   **d** 5000 ml = ___ litres

    e 0.5 km = ___ m   **f** 6 litres = ___ ml

    g 4.5 t = ___ kg   **h** 7 m = ___ cm

    i 30 cl = ___ litres   **j** 0.25 cm = ___ mm

2 Convert these measurements to the units given.

    a 24 km = ___ miles   **b** 85 miles = ___ km

    c 1.5 miles = ___ km   **d** 20 km = ___ miles

    e 4 kg = ___ lb   **f** 6.6 lb = ___ kg

    g 41 kg = ___ lb   **h** 9.9 lb = ___ kg

    i 5 oz = ___ g   **j** 90 g = ___ oz

    Hint: 5 miles ≈ 8 km, 1 kg ≈ 2.2 lb, 1 oz ≈ 30 g.

3 Calculate the area of these shapes. State the units.

    a 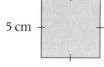   **b**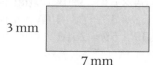

    5 cm   3 mm   7 mm

    c 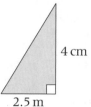   **d**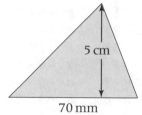

    4 cm   5 cm

    2.5 m   70 mm

                         Hint: units!

4 Calculate the perimeter and area of these shapes.
State the units of your answers.

    a 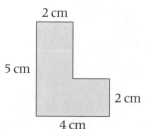   **b**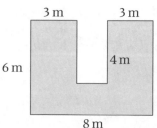

    2 cm   3 m   3 m

    5 cm   6 m   4 m

    2 cm

    4 cm   8 m

1 Calculate the area of these shapes. State the units.

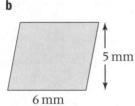

a
3 cm
4 cm

b
5 mm
6 mm

c
2 cm
3 cm
4 cm

d
3 m
5 m
5 m

2 The area of these shapes is given. Calculate the unknown lengths.

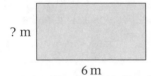

a
? m
6 m
Area = 18 m²

b
3 cm
? cm
Area = 10.5 cm²

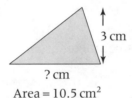

c
? mm
10 mm
Area = 22.5 cm²

d
4 cm
? mm
6 cm
Area = 25 cm²

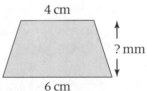

3 Calculate the **i** circumference, and **ii** area, of each circle.

a
3 cm

b
5 cm

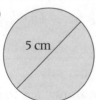

c
4.5 cm

d
3.2 cm

Hint: Circumference = 2πr, Area = πr^2.

4 Using π = 3.14, calculate the radius of each circle.

　a Diameter = 6.3 cm
　b Circumference = 94.2 mm
　c Area = 50.24 cm²
　d Area = 78.5 m²

1 The diagram shows the shape of a classroom that will be covered in carpet. Work out the area of the carpet.

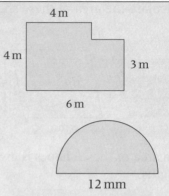

4 m

4 m

3 m

6 m

2 The diagram shows a semi-circle.
The diameter of the semi-circle is 12 mm.

Calculate
i its area
ii its perimeter.

12 mm

Hint: A semi-circle is half a circle.

3 The area of this square is 4 times the area of the triangle. Work out the **perimeter** of the square.

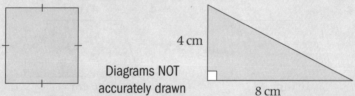

4 cm

Diagrams NOT
accurately drawn

8 cm

4 This is an open top tank in the shape of a cuboid.

The outside of the tank needs to be painted.
1 litre of paint will cover 3 m².
The cost of the paint is £3.99 per litre.

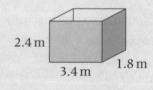

2.4 m

3.4 m   1.8 m

a Calculate the cost of the paint needed to paint the outside of the tank. (If only part of a tin is used you must include the cost of the whole tin.)
b The tank is going to be filled with sand. Work out the maximum amount of sand that the tank will hold.

1 Complete these conversions.

    a ___ m = 670 cm   **b** 3 km = ___ m

    c 1900 mm = ___ cm   **d** 5300 g = ___ kg

    e 6700 ml = ___ litres   **f** 9.5 litres = ___ ml

    g 9 tonnes = ___ kg   **h** 14 kg 200 g = ___ g

    i 56 000 000 cm = ____ km   **j** 0.009 tonnes = ___ g

2 Complete these conversions.

    a 25 miles = ___ kilometres   **b** ___ miles = 28 kilometres

    c 15 cm = ___ inches   **d** ___ kg = 8.8 lb

    e 55 mph = ___ kmph   **f** ___ litres = $14\frac{1}{2}$ pints

    g 20 cm = ___ feet   **h** 30 g = ___ oz

    i 500 ml = ___ pints   **j** 6 kg = ___ lb

    Hint: 5 miles ≈ 8 km, 1 inch ≈ 2.5 cm, 1 foot ≈ 30 cm, 1 kg ≈ 2.2 lb,
         1 pint ≈ 600 ml, 1 oz ≈ 30 g.

3 Calculate the missing area or length in these rectangles:

a

b
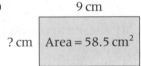

c
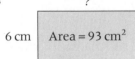

d

4 Calculate the
    i circumference   **ii** area
    of each circle.

a 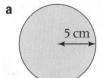   **b** 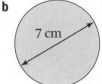   **c**

A1 HW2 Algebraic expressions and indices

1 Simplify these expressions.

   a $3a + b + 3a + 2b$ **b** $5d + 4e - 2d + e + d$

   c $4f + 5g + 6f - 7g + f$ **d** $4h - i + 3h - 5i + h$

   e $3j + 5k + k - 5k - k$ **f** $6l + 4m - 5l - 4m - l + m$

2 An ice cream van sells large ice creams and small ice creams.

The cost of the large ice cream is 90 pence and the small ice cream is 50 pence.

Ice creams

Large   90 pence
Small   50 pence

Write an expression for the cost of buying p large ice creams and s small ice creams.

Simplify   **a** $s^4 \times s^2$ **b** $\dfrac{n^2}{n}$

a $s^4 \times s^2 = s^{(4+2)} = s^6$ **b** $\dfrac{n^2}{n} = n^{(2-1)} = n$

3 Simplify these expressions.

   a $y \times y \times y \times y$ **b** $2 \times r \times r \times r \times s \times s$

   c $3 \times b \times b \times a \times a \times a$ **d** $a^2 \times a^4$

   e $r^3 \times 3r^2$ **f** $b^3 \times b^2 \times b$

   g $3r^2 \times 2r^3$ **h** $5p^3 \times 3q^2$

   i $4b \times 2b^3$ **j** $\dfrac{p^3}{p^2}$

   k $\dfrac{z^5}{z^2}$ **l** $\dfrac{g^3}{g}$

4 Simplify each of these.

   a $\dfrac{a^3 \times a^5}{a^2}$ **b** $\dfrac{q^5 \times q^2}{q^4}$ **c** $\dfrac{k \times k^3}{k^2}$

   d $\dfrac{t \times t^3 \times t^2}{t^4}$ **e** $\dfrac{u^4 \times u^3 \times u^2}{u}$ **f** $\dfrac{s \times s^2 \times s^2}{s^3 \times s}$

   g $\dfrac{p \times p \times p^3}{p^2}$ **h** $\dfrac{r^5 \times r \times r^2}{r^3}$ **i** $\dfrac{v^5 \times v^3 \times v}{v^4}$

Example

Expand and simplify $4(2m + 1) - 2(m + 1)$

$$4(2m + 1) - 2(m + 1) = 8m + 4 - 2m - 2$$
$$= 6m + 2$$

1 Expand and simplify (where necessary) these expressions.

a $3(x + 4)$ **b** $5(x - 3)$

c $4(6 + x)$ **d** $3(x + 5) + x$

e $4(3x - 3) + 2x$ **f** $3(3x + 2) + 3x + 2$

g $6(3x - 3) + 2x$ **h** $5(2x + 1) - 3$

i $2(5x + 5) + 3x - 2$ **j** $7(3x - 3) + 4 - x$

2 Expand and simplify these expressions.

a $3(2x + 3) + 5(2x + 4)$ **b** $4(2x + 4) + 2(4x + 3)$

c $4(3x + 2) + 3(2x + 3)$ **d** $2(3x + 5) + 4(4x + 5)$

e $2(5x + 4) + 4(7x + 3)$ **f** $2(3x + 3) + 5(x + 3)$

g $4(2x + 3) + 4(x - 2)$ **h** $3(2x + 3) + 6(3x + 3)$

i $5(x + 3) + 5(4x - 3)$ **j** $7(2x - 4) + 3(3x + 1)$

3 Expand these expressions.

a $x(3x + 2)$ **b** $x(x^2 + 3)$

c $3x(x^2 - 3)$ **d** $3x(x + 2)$

e $2x(x^2 - 3)$ **f** $4x^2(x^2 + 2)$

g $5x(x^3 + 2)$ **h** $4x(x^2 + 3)$

i $2x^2(x - 4)$ **j** $4x^2(x + 5)$

4 Expand and simplify these expressions.

a $3(x + 3) + 3(x - 2)$ **b** $4(3x + 4) + 3(x - 3)$

c $5(2x + 4) - 4(x + 3)$ **d** $4(3x - 2) - 4(x + 3)$

e $3(3x + 4) - 4(2x - 3)$ **f** $5(x + 3) - 4(2x - 2)$

g $5(2x - 3) - 4(3x - 2)$ **h** $2(2x + 4) + 3(2x - 4)$

i $4(x + 4) - 4(x - 4)$ **j** $2(2x - 1) - 4(x - 1)$

1 Factorise these expressions.

  a $2x + 14$ **b** $5x + 20$

  c $4x + 8$ **d** $3x - 9$

  e $6x + 8$ **f** $12x + 4$

  g $10 - 5x$ **h** $22x + 6$

  i $20 + 4x$ **j** $16x - 10$

2 Factorise these expressions.

  a $x^2 + x$ **b** $3x + x^2$

  c $3x^2 + 3$ **d** $4x^2 + 2x$

  e $3x^3 - 6x$ **f** $5x^4 + x^3$

  g $x^2 - 4x$ **h** $4x - 12x^2$

  i $5x^2 + 25x$ **j** $10x^2 - 2x$

3 a Simplify

    i $4g + 6g$

    ii $3t \times 6p$

  b Expand $6(3y - 4)$

  c Expand and simplify $3(3p + 5) - 3(5p - 6)$

4 a Factorise $x^2 - 4x$

  b Simplify $d^5 \div d^3$

  c Expand and simplify

    i $5(x + 4) + 4(x - 6)$

    ii $3x^2(x + 4) + 3(x^3 - 2)$

5 These cards show expansions and factorisations.
Match the cards in pairs and write out each pair.

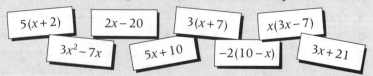

| $5(x + 2)$ | $2x - 20$ | $3(x + 7)$ | $x(3x - 7)$ |

| $3x^2 - 7x$ | $5x + 10$ | $-2(10 - x)$ | $3x + 21$ |

1 Expand and simplify these expressions.

  a $5(6 + x)$ **b** $3(x + 4) + x$
  c $3(3x - 6) + 5x$ **d** $7(3x + 2) + 6x + 2$
  e $7x(x^2 - 6)$ **f** $5x(x + 2)$
  g $4x(x^2 - 2)$ **h** $6x^2(x^2 + 5)$
  i $5(x + 3) + 7(x - 2)$ **j** $5(2x + 6) + 6(x - 3)$
  k $3(5x + 6) - 6(x + 3)$ **l** $3(5x - 2) - 3(x + 3)$

2 Calculate the area and perimeter of these shapes.

a

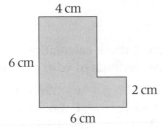

b

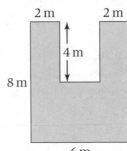

3 **a** List all the factors of 36.
    b List all the factors of 48.
    c Find the highest common factor of 36 and 48.

4 The area of each shape is given. Calculate the unknown length.

a

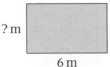

b

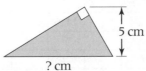

c

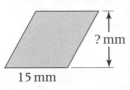

d

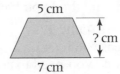

1 Round each of these numbers to the given degree of accuracy.

a 3495 (nearest 100)
b 34.89 (1 decimal place)
c 1234 (nearest 10)
d 0.9847 (2 decimal places)
e 19.834 55 (3 decimal places)
f 3 298 000 (1 significant figure)
g 3.998 (2 significant figures)
h 12 986 (nearest 100)
i 12.0001 (3 decimal places)

2 Write a suitable estimate for each of these calculations.
In each case clearly show how you estimated your answer.

a $21.5 + 23.5$
b $578 - 215$
c 2.98×5.05
d $19.75 \div 3.76$
e 49.98×4.87
f $86.7 \div 2.85$
g $\dfrac{5.6 \times 9.7}{3.87}$
h $\dfrac{29.7 \times 21.3}{39.6}$
i $\dfrac{29.55 \times 2.14^2}{6.1}$

3 Copy and complete the addition square, using a mental method for each calculation.

+	3.4	4.5	2.6	?	4.9	8.5
2.8				7.6		
?						13.2
3.6						
?		11.6				
9.6						
7.1						

4 Use a mental method for each of these calculations.
Write the method you have used.

a Increase 35 by 17.
b Decrease 98 by 45.
c What do you need to add to 745 to get 975?
d How many more than 1398 is 2475?

1 Use a written method to work out

a 54.6 + 74.3	**b** 12.65 + 7. 32	**c** 18.34 + 8.45
d 16.7 − 3.6	**e** 13.95 − 2.24	**f** 9.78 − 3.47
g 143.4 + 5.8	**h** 74.68 + 54.9	**i** 3.667 + 6.418
j 98.46 − 49.54	**k** 69.735 − 14.856	**l** 35.67 − 29.7

2 Use a mental or written method to work out each of the problems.

a Karen sells fish. On Monday she sells 81.4 kg and on Tuesday she sells 66.7 kg. How much fish has Karen sold altogether?

b A bucket full of sand weighs 19.5 kg. The bucket weighs 1.65 kg. How much does the sand weigh?

c James is saving his money in his money box. In July he has £64.36. In August he has £56.95. How much money did James save in August?

d Paula is training to run a marathon. During 4 days of training she runs the following distances: 18.5 miles, 21.95 miles, 11.3 miles and 26.27 miles. Work out the total distance she runs during the 4 days.

3 Use an appropriate method to calculate these. Write each method you have used.

a 34 × 100	**b** 28 × 4	**c** 19 × 6
d 214 ÷ 4	**e** 624 ÷ 8	**f** 12.6 × 21
g 54.8 × 20	**h** 336 ÷ 6	**i** 26.5 × 5
j 3.45 × 2.5	**k** 34 × 2.8	**l** 15 × 0.3

4 Use an appropriate method to work out each of these problems.

a 15 × 46 = 690. What is 15 × 4.6?

b 1 litre of petrol costs 93.4p. How much does 43 litres of petrol cost?

c Sonia buys 32 chocolate bars that cost £9.28. How much does each bar cost?

d Lawson drinks 2.75 litres of water every day. How much water does he drink in 2 weeks?

1 David takes 38 boxes out of his van.
The weight of each box is 25.6 kg.
Work out the **total** weight of the
38 boxes.

2 3.56 × 840 = 2990.4
Write the answer to

  a 0.356 × 8400
  b 2990.4 ÷ 35.6
  c 35.6 × 0.84

3 A pencil is of length 12 cm, measured to the nearest
centimetre.
A pencil case is of length 12.1 cm, measured to the
nearest millimetre.
Explain why it might not be possible for the pencil to fit in
the pencil case.

4 Monique goes to the shops and buys

> 5 kg of potatoes at £0.45 per kg
> 1.54 kg of apples at £1.99 per kg
> 0.5 kg of tomatoes at £0.88 per kg
> 2.2 kg of bananas at £0.85 per kg
> 1.5 kg of carrots at £0.68 per kg
> 0.785 kg of cherries at £8.99 per kg
> 0.61 kg of grapes at £1.87 per kg
> 4 avocados at £0.67 each

  a Work out the total cost of the shopping.
  b Work out the change she would receive from a £20
note.

1 Round each number to the given degree of accuracy.

   a 6795 (nearest 100)

   b 45.45 (1 decimal place)

   c 1564 (nearest 10)

   d 0.6769 (2 decimal places)

   e 2564 (2 significant figures)

   f 59.635 65 (3 decimal places)

   g 6 567 000 (1 significant figure)

   h 15.78 (1 decimal place)

   i 6.998 (2 significant figures)

   j 15 676 (nearest 100)

   k 0.000 566 4 (3 significant figures)

   l 16.0056 (3 decimal places)

2 Use an appropriate method to calculate these. Write the method you have used.

a 67×100	**b** 56×5	**c** 69×8
d $2388 \div 6$	**e** $312 \div 8$	**f** 16.3×24
g 56.6×30	**h** $273 \div 7$	**i** 32.5×6
j 5.29×6.5	**k** 77×5.8	**l** 16×0.5

3 Complete these conversions.

   a 65 cm = ___ mm   **b** 4700 cm = ___ m

   c 6700 g = ___ kg   **d** 600 ml = ___ litres

   e 8 tonnes = ___ kg   **f** 6.6 km = ___ m

   g 15 500 cm = ___ m   **h** 0.9 litres = ___ ml

4 Find the value of each expression.

   a $5d + 6f$ when $d = 6$ and $f = 7$

   b $8m + 2n$ when $m = -5$ and $n = 4$

   c $6p - 6q$ when $p = 20$ and $q = -6$

   d $7e - 3d + f$ when $e = 2$, $d = 5$ and $f = 3$

   e $4b + 9e$ when $b = -5$ and $e = 4$

   f $2t - 4r - s$ when $t = 2$, $r = 4$ and $s = -5$

1 Solve these equations.

    a $a + 10 = 14$ **b** $p + 3 = 10$ **c** $4f = 12$

    d $\dfrac{p}{3} = 5$ **e** $4g = 20$ **f** $t - 4 = 23$

    g $s + 5 = 24$ **h** $6y = 36$ **i** $20 - d = 13$

    j $\dfrac{x}{5} = 9$ **k** $3r = 81$ **l** $100 - r = 54$

2 For each of these 'think of a number' problems
    i   write an equation   **ii** solve the equation.

    a I think of a number and add five. The answer is 30.
    b I think of a number and subtract 4. The answer is 12.
    c I think of a number and multiply it by 7. The answer is 21.
    d I think of a number and divide it by 8. The answer is 4.
    e I think of a number and subtract it from 15. The answer is 8.

3 Solve these equations.

    a $3b + 4 = 13$ **b** $6f - 3 = 9$ **c** $4f + 2 = 22$

    d $\dfrac{p}{3} + 3 = 7$ **e** $5m - 3 = 22$ **f** $\dfrac{r}{4} - 5 = 0$

    g $4d + 6 = 38$ **h** $4r - 10 = -2$ **i** $6k + 4 = 19$

    j $6t + 5 = -13$ **k** $\dfrac{f}{3} + 4 = 1$ **l** $9p - 4 = -31$

4 For each of these 'think of a number' problems
    i   write an equation   **ii** solve the equation.

    a I think of a number, multiply it by 3 then add 2.
       The answer is 17.
    b I think of a number, divide it by 5 then add 6.
       The answer is 10.
    c I think of a number, multiply it by 7 then subtract 8.
       The answer is 20.
    d I think of a number, divide it by 4 then subtract 4.
       The answer is −8.

1 Solve these equations.

a $4n - 6 = 34$

b $\dfrac{s}{3} + 4 = 14$

c $4f + 3 = -17$

d $10 = 3x + 1$

e $20 - 5x = -5$

f $7d + 4 = -10$

g $24 - 5k = 9$

h $\dfrac{g}{4} - 0.5 = 7$

2 The number in each brick is the result of adding the numbers in the two bricks beneath it.
By writing equations find the unknown letter in each wall.

a

	17		
	$4+n$	$n+3$	
4	n	3	

b

	25		
	15	$6+p$	
9	6	p	

c

	24		
	?	?	
q	5	8	

d

	32		
	?	?	
t	4	$3t$	

Show the solution set to the inequality $3x + 4 \leqslant 19$ on a number line.

$3x + 4 \leqslant 19$
$\quad 3x \leqslant 15$
$\quad\; x \leqslant 5$

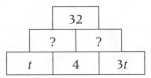

$x \leqslant 5$

3 Solve these inequalities and show the solution set on a number line.

a $3x \leqslant 9$

b $4x > 16$

c $5x \geqslant 15$

d $6x \leqslant 18$

e $3x \leqslant -12$

f $2x \geqslant -20$

4 Solve these inequalities and show the solution set on a number line.

a $4x + 5 > 17$

b $3x - 4 < 5$

c $3x + 1 < -2$

d $5x + 3 \leqslant 23$

e $3x + 5 \geqslant 20$

f $6x + 2 < -16$

1 In these inequalities y is an integer.
For each inequality, write all possible values of y.

  a $-3 < y < -1$

  b $-5 \leqslant y < 2$

  c $4 > y > 1$

  d $6 < 2y < 10$

  e $-4 < 4y \leqslant 16$

2 a Write all the possible values of x in this inequality where x is an integer.

  $-3 < x \leqslant 1$

  b Show all the possible values of x on a number line.

3 Solve these.

  a $3x = 15$

  b $2x + 4 = -4$

  c $\dfrac{x}{3} + 3 = 6$

  d $-10 < 5x \leqslant 15$

4 Solve these equations.

  a $4b + 3 = 15$

  b $20 = 5x - 2.5$

  c $\dfrac{x}{3} - 4 = 3$

  d $100 - 6x = 64$

1 Solve these equations.

   a $6b + 4 = 22$ **b** $5f - 4 = 26$ **c** $7f + 2 = 23$

   d $\dfrac{p}{4} + 3 = 12$ **e** $9m - 12 = 42$ **f** $\dfrac{r}{8} - 5 = -1$

   g $6d + 9 = 63$ **h** $r - 12 = -2$ **i** $6k + 4 = 19$

   j $3t + 5 = -13$ **k** $\dfrac{f}{6} - 6 = -1$ **l** $7p + 11 = -66$

2 Write these numbers in figures.

   a Three thousand and five

   b Twenty two thousand four hundred and four

   c Eleven thousand and twenty two

   d One million and one hundred

   e Nine hundred and ninety nine thousand and ninety nine

3 Write these numbers in words.

   a 67 000   **b** 40 007

   c 687 900   **d** 11 000 000

   e 4 600 007   **f** 699 999

4 Using $\pi = 3.14$, calculate the radius of each circle.

   a Diameter = 5.6 cm   **b** Circumference = 45 mm

   c Area = 153.86 cm^2 **d** Area = 113.04 m^2

5 Write a suitable estimate for each calculation. Clearly show how you estimated your answer.

   a $31.5 + 53.5$ **b** $778 - 615$

   c 3.98×6.15 **d** $29.85 \div 4.76$

   e 79.98×4.21 **f** $99.7 \div 5.15$

   g $\dfrac{9.6 \times 4.7}{5.13}$ **h** $\dfrac{69.7 \times 46.3}{19.6}$

   i $\dfrac{56.55 \times 3.14^2}{6.1}$ **j** $\dfrac{(19.3 \times 1.98) + 9.8^2}{7.15}$

1 Asma did a survey to find out the number of brothers and sisters the students have in her class. The results were

4	2	2	0	1	3	0	0	2
2	3	4	1	4	2	0	2	1
1	0	5	2	2	1	0	4	1

a Draw a tally chart to show this information.

Number of brothers and sisters	Tally	Number of students
0		
1		

b How many students have more than 3 brothers and sisters?

c Calculate how many brothers and sisters the class have in total.

2 These results show how many TVs students' families own.

Number of TVs	0	1	2	3	4	5
Number of students	1	7	12	13	5	1

a How many students were included in the survey?

b Calculate the total number of TVs owned by all of the students.

3 The number of A levels students obtained are

1	3	3	3	2	3	4	3	2
3	3	1	2	2	4	3	2	2
0	1	2	2	3	3	4	3	3

a Is this data collection an observation, a controlled experiment or data logging?

b Draw a suitable data collection sheet for these data.

c Write the most common number of A levels achieved.

d Calculate the total number of A levels achieved.

4 a Describe what is meant by a **random sample**.

b Explain why choosing 15 of your friends to complete a survey is not a random sample.

1 Jimmy surveys people about their personal fitness.
One question in his questionnaire is
How often do you keep fit?
Not very often ☐   *Sometimes* ☐   *Quite often* ☐   *Lots* ☐

   a Write two criticisms of the question.
   b Write a better question.

2 a Devise a question that could have given these data.

Colour	Number of students
Red	3
Light Brown	15
Black	2
Blonde	9
Grey	3

   b Calculate the total number of students in the survey.
   c Make one criticism of the choices of categories for the colour.

3 Decide whether these data are discrete or continuous.

   a The height of students in your class.
   b The shoe size of students in your class.
   c The time it takes to walk to school.
   d The weight of new born babies.
   e The number a dice lands on when tossed 30 times.

4 The heights of students in a class, in metres, are

   1.60   1.45   1.51   1.63   1.70   1.46   1.38   1.44
   1.52   1.39   1.50   1.48   1.60   1.52   1.36   1.70
   1.63   1.55   1.49   1.36   1.45   1.42   1.51   1.67

   a Draw and complete a frequency table, using class intervals
   $1.35 < h \leqslant 1.40$, $1.40 < h \leqslant 1.45$, etc.
   b Which class interval has the most common height?
   c Explain why 1.50 metres cannot be put in the class
   interval $1.50 < h \leqslant 1.55$

1 Class 10B study either French, Spanish or Italian.
The two-way table shows this information.

	French	Spanish	Italian	Total
Male		12		
Female	12		6	22
Total	26		14	

   a Complete the two-way table.

   b How many students were in the class?

2 50 students have to choose to go to the theatre, the art
gallery or the science museum.
     23 of the students are boys.
     8 of the boys choose to visit the theatre.
     9 of the girls choose to visit the art gallery.
     13 of the boys choose to visit the science museum.
     17 of the students choose to visit the theatre.

	Theatre	Art Gallery	Science Museum	Total
Male				
Female				
Total				

   a Copy and complete the two-way table.

   b How many boys chose to go to the art gallery?

3 Here is a record of the heights, in cm, of pea plants.

21 22 11 16 22 13 11 25   9 17 21 24 27
25 12 14   8 12   6 17 19 26 26 18 21 13
23   7 12 26 14   8 12 26 17 19 23 29 21

   a Copy and complete the frequency table.

Height, h, cm	Tally	Frequency
$5 < h \leqslant 10$		
$10 < h \leqslant 15$		
$15 < h \leqslant 20$		
$20 < h \leqslant 25$		
$25 < h \leqslant 30$		

   b How many pea plants were over 20 cm tall?

   c What was the most common height for the pea plants?

1 Freddie recorded the speeds in mph of 27 balls at a cricket match.

62	62	71	48	59	79	79	80	67
35	56	86	75	54	68	60	74	89
65	70	81	77	64	89	53	79	49

a Draw and complete a frequency table, using class intervals, 35–39, 40–49, 50–59, 60–69, 70–79, 80–89.

b Balls over 85 mph are very difficult to return. Find the number of balls over 85 mph.

2 This two-way table shows the number of students at Mansfield School who play hockey and football.

	Hockey	Football
Male	9	55
Female	23	32

a Calculate the number of

   i female students   **ii** hockey players.

b Calculate as fractions, the proportion of students

   i who are male and hockey players   **ii** who are female.

3 Put these measurements in order of size, starting with the smallest.

a 10 miles, 10 kilometres, 55 000 feet

b 35 mph, 60 kmph, 45 mph

c 12 inches, 29 centimetres, 1.2 feet

d 4 pints, 4 litres, 400 ml

Hint: See page 9 for help with these conversions.

4 Solve these inequalities and show the solution set on a number line.

a $5x + 3 > 13$ **b** $8x - 4 < 0$ **c** $4x + 1 < -11$

d $6x - 3 \leqslant 21$ **e** $2x + 5 \geqslant 22$ **f** $10x + 2 < -3$

1 a Cancel each of these fractions into their simplest form.

    i $\frac{2}{10}$ **ii** $\frac{5}{45}$ **iii** $\frac{20}{30}$ **iv** $\frac{40}{55}$

    v $\frac{15}{25}$ **vi** $\frac{27}{81}$ **vii** $\frac{14}{49}$ **viii** $\frac{48}{64}$

b Copy and complete these equivalent fractions.

    i $\frac{1}{2} = \frac{?}{16}$ **ii** $\frac{6}{7} = \frac{24}{?}$ **iii** $\frac{5}{9} = \frac{?}{81}$

    iv $\frac{6}{13} = \frac{?}{65}$ **v** $\frac{24}{32} = \frac{6}{?}$ **vi** $\frac{5}{75} = \frac{1}{?}$

2 Change these fractions to

  a improper fractions

    i $4\frac{3}{5}$ **ii** $6\frac{3}{7}$ **iii** $9\frac{1}{2}$ **iv** $5\frac{4}{5}$

    v $5\frac{3}{4}$ **vi** $10\frac{6}{9}$ **vii** $3\frac{2}{11}$ **viii** $12\frac{3}{5}$

  b mixed numbers

    i $\frac{6}{5}$ **ii** $\frac{9}{4}$ **iii** $\frac{12}{5}$ **iv** $\frac{7}{4}$

    v $\frac{13}{7}$ **vi** $\frac{16}{5}$ **vii** $\frac{17}{5}$ **viii** $\frac{21}{4}$

3 Calculate each of these, giving your answer in its simplest form where appropriate.

  a $\frac{1}{4} + \frac{1}{4}$ **b** $\frac{2}{9} + \frac{4}{9}$ **c** $\frac{10}{19} - \frac{4}{19}$

  d $\frac{4}{15} + \frac{6}{15}$ **e** $\frac{23}{28} - \frac{2}{28}$ **f** $\frac{4}{25} + \frac{14}{25}$

  g $\frac{17}{11} - \frac{6}{11}$ **h** $\frac{12}{7} + \frac{14}{7}$ **i** $\frac{17}{13} - 1$

4 Calculate each of these, giving your answer in its simplest form where appropriate.

  a $\frac{1}{3} + \frac{1}{6}$ **b** $\frac{4}{5} - \frac{3}{10}$ **c** $\frac{1}{3} - \frac{1}{4}$

  d $\frac{3}{7} + \frac{6}{21}$ **e** $\frac{4}{5} + \frac{3}{4}$ **f** $\frac{4}{9} + \frac{3}{4}$

  g $\frac{7}{12} - \frac{1}{7}$ **h** $\frac{4}{5} - \frac{1}{8}$ **i** $\frac{8}{9} + \frac{4}{5}$

Hint: Write both fractions as equivalent fractions with the same denominator.

1 Calculate each of these, leaving your answer in its simplest form.

a $3 \times \frac{2}{5}$ **b** $\frac{4}{5} \times 2$ **c** $\frac{4}{11} \times 3$

d $\frac{2}{7} \times \frac{7}{10}$ **e** $\frac{5}{8} \times \frac{5}{6}$ **f** $\frac{3}{11} \times \frac{1}{3}$

g $7 \times \frac{8}{9}$ **h** $\frac{5}{7} \times \frac{2}{3}$ **i** $\frac{9}{11} \times \frac{3}{5}$

j $3\frac{3}{4} \times 4$ **k** $1\frac{2}{3} \times 9$ **l** $1\frac{1}{2} \times 2\frac{3}{4}$

2 Calculate each of these, leaving your answer in its simplest form.

a $5 \div \frac{7}{8}$ **b** $8 \div \frac{1}{9}$ **c** $9 \div \frac{3}{4}$

d $\frac{2}{5} \div 4$ **e** $\frac{3}{7} \div 3$ **f** $\frac{4}{13} \div \frac{3}{5}$

g $\frac{4}{7} \div \frac{1}{3}$ **h** $\frac{9}{11} \div \frac{3}{7}$ **i** $\frac{1}{2} \div \frac{6}{7}$

j $3\frac{3}{4} \div \frac{1}{3}$ **k** $\frac{8}{9} \div 1\frac{2}{3}$ **l** $3\frac{4}{5} \div 5\frac{1}{4}$

3 Copy and complete the table of equivalent fractions, decimals and percentages. Write fractions in their simplest form.

Fraction	Decimal	Percentage
	0.5	
$\frac{1}{4}$		
		75%
$\frac{1}{3}$		
	0.125	
$\frac{4}{9}$		
		2%
	0.004	
$\frac{1}{13}$		
		8.5%

4 Write five fractions, with different denominators, that will have recurring decimals.

1 Write these numbers in order of size.
Start with the smallest number first.

a 0.5, 22%, $\frac{3}{10}$, 0.45, $\frac{2}{5}$

b $\frac{4}{7}$, 55%, $\frac{5}{11}$, 0.52, $\frac{1}{2}$

c $\frac{7}{12}$, 62%, 0.54, $\frac{2}{3}$, 0.6

d $\frac{3}{4}$, $\frac{7}{9}$, 0.77, $\frac{7}{13}$, 80%

2 a Here are two fractions, $\frac{3}{4}$ and $\frac{2}{3}$.
Explain which is the larger fraction.
You may use the these grids to help your explanation.

b Write these five fractions in order of size.
Start with the smallest fraction.

$\frac{3}{4}$ $\frac{2}{3}$ $\frac{1}{2}$ $\frac{5}{8}$ $\frac{5}{6}$

3 James spent $\frac{1}{5}$ of his pocket money on a cricket set.
He spent $\frac{1}{3}$ of his pocket money on a football.
Work out the fraction of his pocket money he has left.

4 The area of the square is twice the area of the triangle.
Work out the **perimeter** of the square.

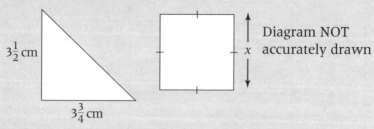

$3\frac{1}{2}$ cm

$3\frac{3}{4}$ cm

Diagram NOT
accurately drawn

x

1 Calculate these and give your answer in its simplest form.

a $\frac{1}{4} + \frac{1}{8}$ **b** $\frac{3}{5} - \frac{3}{10}$ **c** $\frac{1}{3} - \frac{1}{6}$

d $\frac{2}{7} + \frac{3}{14}$ **e** $\frac{1}{5} + \frac{7}{10}$ **f** $\frac{4}{9} + \frac{1}{3}$

g $\frac{7}{4} - \frac{1}{5}$ **h** $\frac{4}{7} - \frac{1}{3}$ **i** $\frac{1}{7} + \frac{4}{5}$

Hint: Write both fractions as equivalent fractions with the same denominator.

2 Write these numbers in order of size.
Start with the smallest number.

a 0.98, 0.9, 0.011, 0.646, 0.099

b $\frac{3}{4}, \frac{3}{8}, \frac{1}{5}, \frac{6}{7}, \frac{7}{9}$

c 0.45, $\frac{4}{7}$, 65%, $\frac{2}{3}, \frac{7}{9}$

3 Copy and complete the table of equivalent fractions, decimals and percentages. Write fractions in their simplest form.

Fraction	Decimal	Percentage
	0.4	
$\frac{3}{4}$		
		25%
$\frac{2}{3}$		
		12.5%
$\frac{3}{10}$		
		1%
$\frac{1}{12}$	0.005	
		65%

4 Simplify each of these.

a $\dfrac{b^4 \times b^3}{b^2}$ **b** $\dfrac{t^5 \times t^2}{t^5}$ **c** $\dfrac{m \times m^6}{m^2}$

d $\dfrac{t^5 \times t^3 \times t^2}{t}$ **e** $\dfrac{n^3 \times n^6 \times n}{n^3}$ **f** $\dfrac{p \times p^2 \times p^2}{p^3 \times p}$

1 Calculate the size of the angles marked by letters.

a 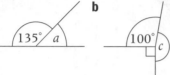 **b**

c   **d**

2 Calculate the size of the angles marked by letters.

a 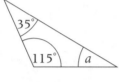 **b**  **c**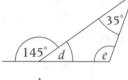

d 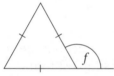 **e**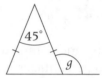

3 Work out the size of the angles marked by letters.
Give a reason for each answer.

a 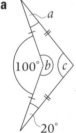 **b** 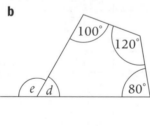 **c**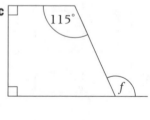

4 Calculate the value of *x* for each question.

a 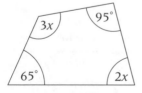 **b**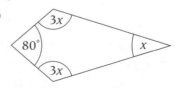

1 Calculate the sum of the interior angles of a

   a pentagon
   b hexagon   Hint: Split the shapes into triangles.
   c nonagon
   d decagon.

2 Calculate the size of

   i one interior angle
   ii one exterior angle

   of a regular

   a quadrilateral
   b octagon   Hint: Exterior angles add to 360°.
   c heptagon
   d dodecagon.

3 The interior angle of a regular polygon is 120°.

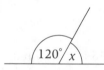

   a Calculate the size of the exterior angle x.
   b Calculate the number of sides of the
      regular polygon.
   c What is the mathematical name for this polygon?

4 A regular polygon has 20 sides.

   a Calculate the size of an exterior angle.
   b Calculate the size of an interior angle.

5 Calculate the size of the unknown angles in these polygons.

   a
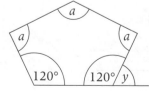
   b
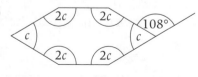

1 AB and CD are parallel.
Find the size of the angles marked
x and y.
Give reasons for your answers.

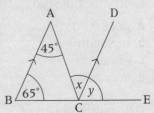

2 AB is parallel to CD.
Find the angle marked x.
Give reasons for your
answer.

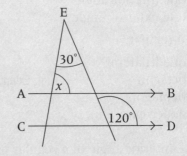

3 Work out the sizes of
the angles marked a,
b and c. Give reasons
for your answers.

QRS is a straight line

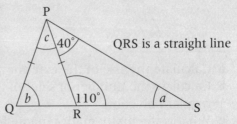

4 The diagram below is part of a
pattern. It is made up of a regular
pentagon, squares and an isosceles
triangle.

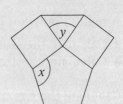

   a Write the size of the angle
marked x.

   b Work out the size of the angle
marked y.

1 Calculate the size of the missing angles in each diagram.

a

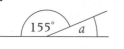

b

c

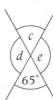

d

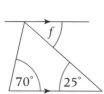

e

f

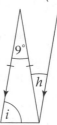

2 For each of these 'think of a number' problems
   i write an equation **ii** solve the equation.

  a I think of a number, multiply it by 2, then add 4.
     The answer is 14.
  b I think of a number divide, it by 4, then add 6.
     The answer is 11.
  c I think of a number multiply, it by 6, then subtract 8.
     The answer is −10.

3 Claire uses a questionnaire to find out what people think
  about sport.
  Two questions in her questionnaire are

   What sports do you like?

   Don't you think that exercise is good for you?

  Give one criticism of each question and suggest
  improvements.

4 For each pair of fractions choose either < or > to show which
  fraction is greater.

  a $\frac{1}{4}$ and $\frac{1}{5}$ **b** $\frac{9}{10}$ and $\frac{9}{12}$ **c** $\frac{7}{10}$ and $\frac{4}{5}$

  d $\frac{4}{5}$ and $\frac{19}{25}$ **e** $\frac{5}{12}$ and $\frac{1}{4}$ **f** $\frac{29}{100}$ and $\frac{3}{10}$

1 Write out the first five terms of these sequences.

   a 1st term 4, increases by 5 each time
   b 3rd term 5, decreases by 3 each time
   c 2nd term 8, increases by 2 each time
   d 3rd term −1, increases by 4 each time
   e 2nd term 0, decreases by 3 each time
   f 5th term 6, increases by 3 each time

2 For each of these sequences

   i work out the three missing terms
   ii describe the sequence.

   a 4, 7, __, 13, 16, __, 22, __
   b 20, __, 12, 8, 4, __, __
   c 7, 5, __, 1, __, __
   d __, 10, 8, __, __, 2
   e __, −15, −11, __, __, 1
   f __, 15, __, 3, __

3 Find the first 3 terms and the 10th term of the sequences
with nth term

   a $4n + 4$
   b $5n + 2$
   c $6n − 4$
   d $3n + 5$
   e $10n + 3$
   f $10 − 2n$

4 Find the first 5 terms of the sequences with nth term

   a $n^2 + 3$
   b $n^2 − 3$
   c $2n^2 + 3$
   d $3n^2 − 4$
   e $10 − n^2$
   f $4n^2 − 5$

1 Copy and complete these tables for linear sequences.

a
Pattern number	1	2	3	4	5	*n*
Term	4	10		22	28	

b
Pattern number	1	2	3	4	5	*n*
Term	15	18		24		

c
Pattern number	1	2	3	4	5	*n*
Term		−5	−3		1	

2 Find the *n*th term for these sequences.

   a 12, 14, 16, 18, 20, ...
   b 7, 12, 17, 22, 27, ...
   c 10, 19, 28, 37, 46, ...
   d 25, 22, 19, 16, 13, 10, ...
   e −3, −1, 1, 3, 5, 7, ...
   f −6, −9, −12, −15, −18, −21, ...

3 Here is a sequence.

   a Write the number of squares in the next two patterns.
   b Find, in terms of *n*, an expression for the number of squares in the *n*th pattern.
   c Find the number of squares in the 50th pattern.

4 Repeat question **3** for this sequence of dots.

1 Here is a pattern made from matchsticks.

   a Draw the next pattern in the sequence.
   b Copy and complete the table.

Pattern number	1	2	3	4	5	n
Term						

   c Use the general formula to work out how many matchsticks are needed for the 10th pattern.

2 Here is a pattern of hexagons.

   a Copy and complete the table.

Pattern number	1	2	3	4	5	n
Term						

   b Use the general formula to work out how many hexagons are needed for the 50th pattern.

3 Here is a pattern of triangles.

   Work out, using the general formula, how many triangles there will be in the 20th pattern.

4 Find the nth term for this sequence
    10, 14, 18, 22, 26, 30, ...

1 Draw each angle and state what type of angle it is.

   a 55°   **b** 190°   **c** 265°   **d** 25°   **e** 315°

2 For each sequence, find
   i the next three terms
   ii the nth term.

   a 3, 5, 7, 9, ...
   b 35, 32, 29, 26, ...
   c 7, 13, 19, 25, 31, ...
   d 10, 6, 2, −2, −6, ...
   e −14, −11, −8, −5, ...

3 Derek recorded the heights, in cm, of the plants in his garden.

11	22	21	6	22	13	11	25	9	17	21	24	17
25	22	14	28	12	6	27	19	26	26	29	11	23
8	7	22	16	14	8	12	26	17	19	13	29	21

   a Copy and complete the frequency table for these data.

Height, h, cm	Tally	Frequency
$5 < h \leqslant 10$		
$10 < h \leqslant 15$		
$15 < h \leqslant 20$		
$20 < h \leqslant 25$		
$25 < h \leqslant 30$		

   b How many plants were over the height of 15 cm?
   c What was the most common height for the plants?

4 Calculate each of these and leave your answer in simplest form.

   a $\frac{1}{3} \times \frac{2}{5}$ **b** $\frac{3}{7} \times \frac{1}{3}$ **c** $\frac{9}{10} \times \frac{4}{5}$

   d $\frac{3}{4} \times \frac{7}{9}$ **e** $\frac{5}{7} \times \frac{1}{4}$ **f** $\frac{1}{2} \times \frac{5}{9}$

   g $\frac{2}{3} \div \frac{3}{5}$ **h** $\frac{3}{7} \div \frac{5}{6}$ **i** $\frac{5}{12} \div \frac{4}{5}$

   j $\frac{4}{5} \div \frac{2}{3}$ **k** $\frac{9}{10} \div \frac{1}{8}$ **l** $\frac{3}{5} \div \frac{3}{7}$

1 60 people were asked to name their favourite colour.

The results are shown in the table.

Draw a bar chart to represent this information.

Colour	Frequency
Red	15
Blue	12
Green	18
Purple	5
Black	2
Other	8

2 180 people were asked what was their favourite sport. The results were

a Calculate the number of people who liked other sports.

b Calculate the angle one person represents in a pie chart.

c Calculate the angle of each category in the pie chart.

d Draw the pie chart.

Sport	Frequency
Football	64
Cricket	31
Rugby	28
Golf	29
Tennis	15
Other	?

3 The heights, in cm, of plants in a garden were recorded.
Draw a histogram to show the heights of the plants.

Height, h, cm	Frequency
$5 < h \leqslant 10$	6
$10 < h \leqslant 15$	13
$15 < h \leqslant 20$	16
$20 < h \leqslant 25$	9
$25 < h \leqslant 30$	4

4 The time taken by 120 runners in the Lake Vryney half marathon were recorded.

Draw a frequency polygon to illustrate this information.

Time, t, hours	Frequency
$1 < t \leqslant 1.25$	14
$1.25 < t \leqslant 1.5$	26
$1.5 < t \leqslant 1.75$	35
$1.75 < t \leqslant 2$	24
$2 < t \leqslant 2.25$	18
$2.25 < t \leqslant 2.5$	3

1 The resting pulse rates, in beats per minute (bpm), of 30 athletes are

56	74	63	72	83	49	58	59	79	48
73	77	89	57	64	61	69	75	76	81
70	72	84	52	44	57	74	75	81	77

Draw an ordered stem-and-leaf diagram to represent this information. Choose suitable stems.

2 The heights of students in a class, in metres, to the nearest cm, are

1.60	1.45	1.51	1.63	1.70	1.46	1.38	1.44
1.52	1.39	1.50	1.48	1.60	1.52	1.36	1.70
1.63	1.55	1.49	1.36	1.45	1.42	1.51	1.67

Draw an ordered stem-and-leaf diagram to represent this information. Choose suitable stems.

3 Stephen is on a diet and his weight in kg is recorded over 10 months. His weight each month is shown.

Month	Jan	Feb	Mar	Apr	May	Jun	Jul	Aug	Sept	Oct
Weight in kg	108	103	101	99	97	94	93	95	94	94

Draw a line graph to show his weight.

4 The exam pass rate of the percentage of students gaining 5 A*–C GCSE grades for a school over 9 years is shown.

Year	1997	1998	1999	2000	2001	2002	2003	2004	2005
% 5 A*–C	37	39	41	50	54	56	60	62	59

Draw a line graph to show the percentages of 5 A*–C GCSE grades.

1 10 men took part in a long jump competition. The table shows the heights of the 10 men and the best jumps they made.

Height of men (m)	1.70	1.80	1.65	1.75	1.65	1.74	1.60	1.75	1.60	1.67
Best jump (m)	5.33	6.00	5.00	5.95	4.80	5.72	4.60	5.80	4.40	5.04

a Plot the points on a scatter diagram.
b Describe in words the relationship between the height of the men and the maximum distance they jumped.
c State the type of correlation shown in this graph.

2 The table shows the number of units of electricity used in heating a house on ten different days and the average temperature for each day.

Average Temperature (°C)	6	2	0	6	3	5	10	8	9	12
Units of electricity used	28	38	41	34	31	31	22	25	23	22

a Plot the points on a scatter diagram.
b Describe in words the relationship between the average temperature and the number of units of electricity used.
c State the type of correlation shown in this graph.

3 In a town, 1800 cars were stolen in a year. The table below shows the times of the day when they were stolen.

Time	Number of cars
Midnight to 6 am	700
6 am to midday	80
Midday to 6 pm	280
6 pm to midnight	470
Time unknown	270

Draw a pie chart to show this information.

1 A regular polygon has 10 sides.

  a Calculate the size of an exterior angle.

  b Calculate the size of an interior angle.

2 Simplify these expressions.

  a $4x + y + 3x$ **b** $8x - y + 2y$

  c $x - 3y + 2x$ **d** $x - 4y + 6z - 5x - 6x + y$

  e $6x + y - 4x - y + 2x$ **f** $9x - 4y + 2x - 6y$

  g $x + y - x - y$ **h** $9x + 6y - z - 4y + 2z$

3 Melissa asked 90 people what their favourite type of film was. She recorded the results in this table and used it to complete a pie chart.

Film	Frequency	Angle
Thriller	13	
Comedy	29	
Horror	5	
Science Fiction	21	
Romance	12	
Action	?	

  a Calculate the number of people who liked Action films.

  b Calculate the angle that will represent one person in the pie chart.

  c Calculate the angle for each category in the pie chart.

  d Draw the pie chart.

4 This table shows the height and weight of 10 people.

  a Plot the points on a scatter diagram.

  b Describe in words the relationship between the height and weight of the 10 people.

  c State the type of correlation shown in this graph.

Height in cm	Weight in kg
165	56
172	64
155	52
184	70
149	50
181	72
167	60
149	48
177	62
156	53

1 For each of these functions

   i draw a function machine

   ii work out the outputs for the inputs −2, −1, 0, 1, 2, 3.

   a $4x + 2$ **b** $5x - 3$

   c $\frac{1}{2}x + 4$ **d** $4x - 10$

2 Match each of these function machines to a set of coordinates.

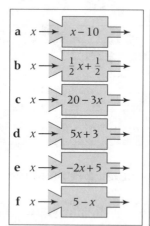

a $x \rightarrow \boxed{x - 10} \rightarrow$ **A** $(-2, 26)(-1, 23)(0, 20)(1, 17)(2, 14)$

b $x \rightarrow \boxed{\frac{1}{2}x + \frac{1}{2}} \rightarrow$ **B** $(-2, -7)(-1, -2)(0, 3)(1, 8)(2, 13)$

c $x \rightarrow \boxed{20 - 3x} \rightarrow$ **C** $(-2, 7)(-1, 6)(0, 5)(1, 4)(2, 3)$

d $x \rightarrow \boxed{5x + 3} \rightarrow$ **D** $(-2, 9)(-1, 7)(0, 5)(1, 3)(2, 1)$

e $x \rightarrow \boxed{-2x + 5} \rightarrow$ **E** $(-2, -\frac{1}{2})(-1, 0)(0, \frac{1}{2})(1, 1)(2, 1\frac{1}{2})$

f $x \rightarrow \boxed{5 - x} \rightarrow$ **F** $(-2, -12)(-1, -11)(0, -10)(1, -9)(2, -8)$

3 a Copy and complete the table of values for $y = 4x - 2$.

x	−2	−1	0	1	2
y					

   b Write the coordinate pairs.

   c Plot the line $y = 4x - 2$ onto a grid with appropriate axes.

4 a Copy and complete the table of values for $y = -2x + 4$.

x	−2	−1	0	1	2
y					

   b Write the coordinate pairs.

   c Plot the line $y = -2x + 4$ onto a grid with appropriate axes.

A4 HW3 Harder linear graphs

1 On a copy of the grid, draw graphs of these functions.

  a $y = 3x + 1$
  b $y = 2x + 1$
  c $y = -3x + 1$
  d $y = -2x + 1$
  e What do you notice about the functions and their graphs?

2 a On a copy of the grid, draw the graph of $x + y = 4$.
  b Rearrange the equation to make y the subject.
  c i Use your equation to find y when x equals 3.
    ii Use your graph to check your answer.
  d Use your graph to find x when y equals 2.5.

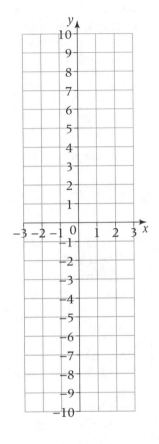

3 Draw these graphs on the same set of axes.

  a $y = 4$ **b** $x = -2$
  c $y = 0$ **d** $x = 6$
  e Write the coordinates where

    i $y = 4$ and $x = -2$ cross
    ii $y = 0$ and $x = 6$ cross.
    iii What do you notice?

  f Without drawing the graphs of $y = 6$ and $x = -2$, what will be the coordinates where they cross?

4 a Draw the graph of $y = 2x - 1$.
  b On the same set of axes draw the graph of $y = 5$.
  c Write the coordinates of point P where the graphs cross.

1 Match the equations to the graphs of straight lines.

$y = -3$

$y = x - 3$

$x = -3$

$x = 2$

$y = 2$

$y = -3x - 2$

$y = 2x + 2$

$y = -\frac{1}{2}x + 2$ $y = -x - 3$

Hint: Beware, there are some extra equations!

2 ABCD is a parallelogram.
A is the point (0, 3).
C is the point (0, −3).
The equation of the straight line through A and B is $y = \frac{1}{2}x + 3$.

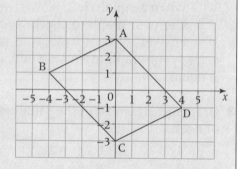

a Find the equation of the line through C and D.

b Find the equation of the line passing through A and D.

3 a Copy and complete the table of values for $y = 3x + 2$.

x	−2	−1	0	1	2	3
y		−1	2			

b On a grid, draw the graph of $y = 3x + 2$.

c Use your graph to find

   i the value of y when $x = -1.5$

   ii the value of x when $y = 3.5$.

4 Write three equations of straight lines that are parallel to

   a $y = 4x - 5$ **b** $y = -5x - 5$

1 Write the *n*th term of each sequence.

   a 3, 7, 11, 15, 19, 23, ...
   b 6, 8, 10, 12, 14, 16, ...
   c 12, 15, 18, 21, 24, 27, ...
   d 19, 25, 31, 37, 43, ...
   e 10, 9, 8, 7, 6, 5, 4, ...

2 Simplify these fractions.

   a $\frac{4}{5} + \frac{2}{5}$ **b** $\frac{3}{4} + \frac{3}{4}$ **c** $\frac{1}{8} + \frac{5}{8}$

   d $\frac{9}{10} + \frac{3}{10}$ **e** $\frac{4}{5} + \frac{7}{10}$ **f** $\frac{6}{7} + \frac{3}{14}$

   g $\frac{4}{5} + \frac{5}{6}$ **h** $\frac{4}{7} + \frac{1}{3}$ **i** $\frac{5}{12} + \frac{3}{5}$

3 a Copy and complete this table for the function $y = 2x + 3$.

x	0	1	2	3	4	5
y						

   b On a copy of the grid, draw the graph of $y = 2x + 3$.

   c Draw the lines $y = 4$ and $x = 3$ on the same grid.

   d Use part **c** to solve these equations.

   i $2x + 3 = 4$
   ii $2x + 3 = 3$

4 Put these measurements in order of size, starting with the smallest.

   a 5 miles, 5 km, 6000 m
   b 1.5 kg, 1700 g, 1 tonne
   c 20 inches, 1 metre, 6 feet
   d 1000 mm, 1 m, 10 cm
   f 10 lb, 10 kg, 100 ounces

Hint: See page 9 for help with these conversions.

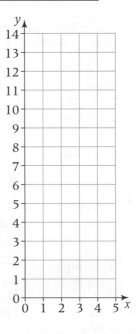

1 A fair dice, numbered 1–6, is rolled. Calculate the probability that the dice will land on

a a 6   **b** an odd number

c a square number   **d** a cube number

e a prime number   **f** a multiple of 3

g a factor of 12   **h** a 7.

2 A bag of sweets contains these flavours

4 strawberry

3 orange

2 blackcurrant

5 lemon

Calculate the probability of picking

a an orange sweet

b a lemon sweet

c a raspberry sweet.

3 The letters of the word MATHEMATICS are put into a bag. One letter is taken out at random.
Calculate the probability that the letter is

a an M

b not an M

c a vowel

d a consonant

e not an A

f a B.

4 The possible outcomes in a football match are win, lose or draw. The probability that Fowey Town Football Club win, lose or draw is shown in this table.

Outcome	Win	Lose	Draw
Probability	0.65	0.25	?

a Calculate the probability that Fowey Town will draw.

b What is the most likely outcome?

1 A box of chocolates contains milk and plain chocolates. Some of these chocolates contain nuts. The two-way table shows the number of chocolates in each category.

	Milk chocolate	Plain chocolate
Contains nuts	5	7
Does not contain nuts	12	8

One chocolate is selected at random.

Calculate the probability that the chocolate is a

a plain chocolate that contains nuts   **b** milk chocolate
c chocolate that contains nuts   **d** plain chocolate
e milk chocolate that contains nuts

2 Students at a school play either hockey, football or rugby. The two-way table shows information about these students.

	Hockey	Football	Rugby	Total
Male	14			45
Female		25	7	
Total	29	56		

a Copy and complete the two-way table.
b How many students were in the class?
c Calculate the probability that a student chosen at random is a

i hockey player   **ii** male and a football player
iii female   **iv** female and a rugby player

3 If a dice is rolled 300 times, how many times would you expect it to land on

a a 6   **b** an even number
c a factor of 8   **d** an 8?

4 The probability of Zahir being early or on time for work is 0.76.

a Calculate the probability of his being late for work.
b Over 300 work days, how many times would you expect him to be late for work?

1 A dice is to be thrown.
The probability that this dice will land on each of the
numbers 1 to 6 is given in the table.

Number	1	2	3	4	5	6
Probability	x	0.1	0.3	0.2	0.2	0.1

The dice is to be thrown once.

a Calculate the value of x.

b Calculate the probability that the dice will land on a
number higher than 4.

The dice is thrown 500 times.

c Estimate the number of times the dice is likely to land
on a six.

2 Tony carries out a survey about the words in a book.
He chooses a page at random.
He then counts the number of letters in each of the first
50 words on the page. The results are

3	3	5	5	6	7	1	3	4	7
4	7	2	3	4	4	3	5	1	5
2	6	6	5	4	3	4	3	4	1
6	5	5	4	2	5	1	5	6	4
1	4	1	2	6	5	4	4	3	4

a Draw a frequency table to show these results.

b State the modal number of letters.

c A word is chosen at random. Calculate the probability
that it has 4 letters.

d The book has 20 000 words. Estimate the number of
4-letter words in the book.

3 The probability that a new car is faulty is 0.09. Calculate
the probability that it is not faulty.

4 Samira does a statistical experiment. She throws a dice
600 times. She scores six 150 times.
Is the dice fair? Explain your answer.

1 The letters of the word ISOSCELES are put into a bag. A letter is taken out at random. What is the probability of picking

   a E   **b** S   **c** a vowel?

2 The average exam performance of two schools over 6 years is

Year	2000	2001	2002	2003	2004	2005
School A	34%	38%	35%	40%	45%	46%
School B	56%	52%	54%	48%	44%	40%

  a Copy the grid and draw line graphs to show this information.

  b Describe what has happened to the percentages in the two schools over the 6 years.

  c What happened between 2003 and 2004?

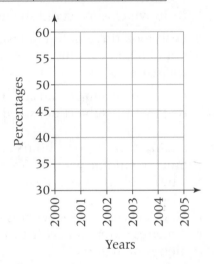

3 Giving reasons for your answers, calculate
  a angle ABC
  b angle ADC.

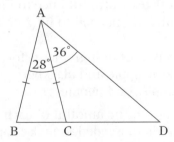

4 Expand and simplify these expressions.

   a $3(x+4)$ **b** $4x(x+5)$ **c** $2x(x-5)$ **d** $x^2(x+4x)$

1 Put these in order of size starting with the smallest.

   a $\frac{3}{5}$, 65%, $\frac{7}{8}$, 0.7   **b** 0.45, 49%, $\frac{4}{9}$, $\frac{4}{10}$

   c 33%, $\frac{1}{3}$, 25%, 0.3   **d** 99%, 1, $\frac{9}{10}$, 0.999

   e $\frac{4}{13}$, 25%, 0.09, $\frac{1}{5}$ **f** 0.15, 13%, $\frac{1}{13}$, $\frac{2}{23}$

2 **a** Michelle took three tests. In Maths she scored 63 out of 72, in Science she scored 44 out of 60 and in RE she scored 29 out of 50.

   i In which subject did she do best?
   ii In which subject did she do worst?

   b Leah took three different tests. In English she scored 58 out of 80, in Graphics she scored 57 out of 72 and in PE she scored 51 out of 60.

   i In which subject did she do best?
   ii In which subject did she do worst?

3 **a** Shahzad works for 5 hours and gets paid £23.25. How much would he get paid for 7 hours?
   b 4 boxes of crisps cost £9.40. What is the cost of 7 boxes of crisps?
   c 40 rulers cost £8.80. What is the cost of 9 rulers?
   d 7 metres of material cost £13.93. What is the cost of 3 metres of material?
   e It takes 5 litres of juice to fill 40 cups. How many litres of juice are needed to fill 25 cups?

4 This is a list of ingredients for making apple and blackberry crumble for 4 people.

   Work out the amount of each ingredient needed to make apple and blackberry crumble for 14 people.

   Ingredients for 4 people

   80 g plain flour
   60 g butter
      4 cooking apples
   90 g soft brown sugar
   100 g blackberries

N4 HW3 Direct proportion and exchange rates

1 a Manjit cuts a piece of string into two pieces. Piece A is 12 cm long and piece B is 16 cm long.

   i How many times longer is piece B compared to piece A?

   ii What proportion of the length of piece B is piece A?

b James is 8 years old and his Auntie Claire is 32 years old.

   i How many times older is Claire compared to James?

   ii What proportion of Claire's age is James' age?

2 Here is a recipe to make 8 shortbread biscuits.

150 g plain white flour   100 g butter
45 ml rice flour   50 g caster sugar

a How much caster sugar would you need to make 10 shortbread biscuits?

b Pam has 1 kg of plain white flour. She has plenty of the other ingredients. What is the maximum number of shortbread biscuits she could make?

3 Use this exchange rate to convert between each currency.

£1 = $1.84

a Convert these amounts of money into US dollars.

   i £55   **ii** £1000   **iii** £750

b Convert these amounts of money into pounds.

   i $250   **ii** $1500   **iii** $1 000 000

4 Sonia went skiing in France. She changed £250 into euros when the exchange rate was £1 = €1.44.

a Work out how many euros she received.

When she returned she had €125 left. The new exchange rate was £1 = €1.41.

b Work out how much Sonia got in pounds for her €125.

1 Sian travels 20 miles from her house to the shops in 30 minutes.

  a Work out Sian's speed.
  Give your answer in mph.

  Sian spends 1 hour at the shops then travels back home at a speed of 60 mph.

  b How long does it take her to get home?

2 The cost of 16 pens is £29.60.

  Work out the cost of 9 pens.

3 Jason fills a pool with 55 000 gallons of water.
  He paid £128.70 for the 55 000 gallons of water.
  Work out how much it would cost to fill a pool that holds 75 000 gallons of water.

4 Brian and Wendy travelled from Coventry to London by car.
  The distance from Coventry to London is 157.5 miles.
  The journey took 1 h 45 min.

  a Work out their average speed.

  The car used 17 litres of petrol on the journey.

  b How many litres of petrol would a 200 mile journey use (assuming they were travelling at the same speed)?

1 Copy the grid, extend the axes to +10, and draw these straight line graphs.

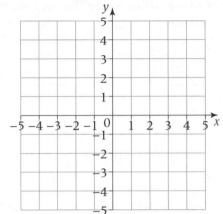

a $y = 4x + 4$
b $y = 2x - 3$
b $y = 3x$
c $y = -2x + 1$

2 Calculate the area of each shape. State the units.

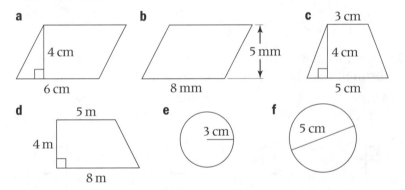

a 4 cm, 6 cm

b 5 mm, 8 mm

c 3 cm, 4 cm, 5 cm

d 5 m, 4 m, 8 m

e 3 cm

f 5 cm

3 Calculate the speeds in miles per hour of each vehicle.

   a Vehicle A travelling 300 miles in 5 hours
   b Vehicle B travelling 100 miles in 1 hour 30 minutes
   c Vehicle C travelling 96 miles in 1.2 hour
   d Vehicle D travelling 50 miles in 30 minutes

4 The probability of Karl being early or on time for work is 0.85.

   a Calculate the probability of Karl being late for work.
   b Over 200 work days, how many times would you expect him to be late for work?

53

1 Copy and complete the diagrams to reflect the shape in the mirror lines.

a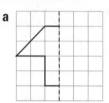

b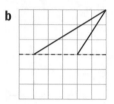

c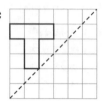

2 Give the equation of the mirror line for each reflection.

a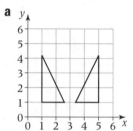

b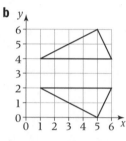

c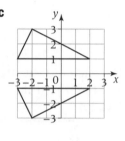

3 Copy the shapes onto squared paper. Rotate the shapes through the given angle and direction about the dot.

a 90°
clockwise

b 180°
clockwise

c 90°
anticlockwise

d 180°
anticlockwise

   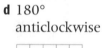

4 Copy the shape and grid onto squared paper.

   a Reflect the triangle A in the line $x = 1$. Label it B.

   b Rotate the triangle B by 180° about the point (1, 0). Label it C.

   c Describe the single transformation that maps triangle A onto triangle C.

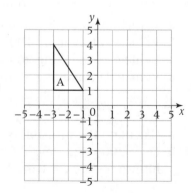

Translations and congruence

1 Describe these transformations.

  a A to B   **b** A to C

  c B to C   **d** B to D

  e C to D   **f** C to E

  g D to E   **h** D to A

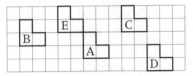

2 On squared paper, draw axes from −5 to 5 in x and y.

  a Plot and join the points (−3, 1) (−1, 1) (−1, 3) (−3, 4).
    Label it shape A. Name the shape.

  b Translate shape A by

    i $\begin{pmatrix} 5 \\ 1 \end{pmatrix}$ Label it B.   **ii** $\begin{pmatrix} -1 \\ -5 \end{pmatrix}$ Label it C.   **iii** $\begin{pmatrix} 4 \\ -4 \end{pmatrix}$ Label it D.

3 Which pairs of triangles are congruent?

  a i   **ii**   **iii**

  b i   **ii**   **iii**

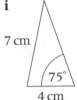  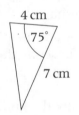

4 Copy the shape and grid onto squared paper.

  a Reflect the triangle A in the x axis. Label it B.

  b Rotate the triangle B by 90° clockwise about the origin. Label it C.

  c Describe the single transformation that maps triangle A onto triangle C.

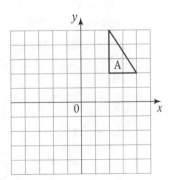

55

1 Copy the rectangle.
   a Draw all of the lines of symmetry on the shape.
   b Write the the order of rotational symmetry.

2 Copy the 3-dimensional shape.

   a Draw on one plane of symmetry.
   b Write the mathematical name for the shape.

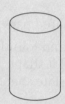

3 Copy the grid.
   Shape A is rotated anticlockwise, centre (1, 0), to shape B.
   Shape B is rotated anticlockwise, centre (1, 0), to shape C.
   Shape C is rotated anticlockwise, centre (1, 0), to shape D.

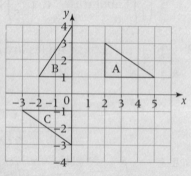

   a Mark the position of shape D.
   b Describe the single transformation that takes shape C to shape A.

4 Copy the grid.
   The triangle R has been drawn on the grid.

   a Reflect the triangle R in the line $x = 3$. Label the image S.
   b Rotate triangle S through 90° clockwise about (1, −1). Label it T.
   c Describe the single transformation that maps shape R onto shape T.

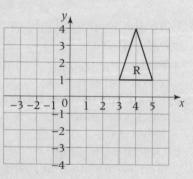

1 The exchange rate for euros to pounds is approximately
£1 = €1.40
Calculate how many euros would you get for

a £10   **b** £15   **c** £120   **d** £500

Calculate how many pounds you would get for

e €5.60   **f** €154   **g** €168   **h** €224

2 Copy the shape and grid
onto squared paper.

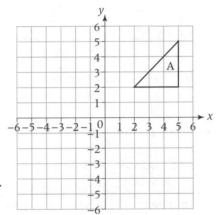

a Reflect triangle A in the
y-axis. Label it B.
b Rotate triangle B 90°
anticlockwise about the
origin and label it C.
c Describe the single
transformation that maps
triangle A onto triangle C.

3 A dice is to be thrown which is not fair. The probability that
this dice will land on each of the numbers 1 to 6 is given in
the table.

Number	1	2	3	4	5	6
Probability	0.2	0.2	0.1	0.3	x	0.1

The dice is to be thrown once.

a Calculate the probability of it landing on a 5.
b Calculate the probability that the dice will land on an even
number.

4 Put these numbers in order of size starting with the smallest.

a $\frac{1}{3}$, $\frac{3}{5}$, 35%, 0.3, 0.29.

b $\frac{2}{3}$, 60%, 0.62, $\frac{3}{7}$, 0.6.

c 0.12, 24%, $\frac{1}{24}$, $\frac{1}{12}$, 0.24.

1 Use the trial and improvement method to find the square root of each of these numbers to 1 decimal place. Record your results in a table. The first one has been started for you.

a $\sqrt{90}$

Estimate	Check (square of estimate)	Answer	Too big or too small
9	9^2	81	Too small
10	10^2	100	Too big
9.5			

b $\sqrt{70}$ **c** $\sqrt{120}$ **d** $\sqrt{250}$

2 Some numbers can be represented as the sum of two squares.
For example, $4^2 + 5^2 = 16 + 25 = 41$

Find all the numbers between 1 and 50 that can be represented as the sum of two square numbers.

3 Use the trial and improvement method to find the cube root of each of these numbers to 2 decimal places. Record your results in a table.

a $\sqrt[3]{10}$ **b** $\sqrt[3]{60}$ **c** $\sqrt[3]{135}$ **d** $\sqrt[3]{400}$

4 a A cube has a volume of 216 cm³.
What are its dimensions?

    b Between which two whole numbers does $\sqrt[3]{30}$ lie?
Explain your answer.

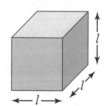

1 Use the x^y-button on your calculator to work out these questions. In each case, copy the question and find the value of x.

a $4^x = 16$ **b** $5^x = 125$ **c** $10^x = 1\,000\,000$
d $x^4 = 4096$ **e** $2^x = 1024$ **f** $x^{10} = 1$
g $3^x = 531\,441$ **h** $x^9 = 10\,077\,696$ **i** $19^x = 1$

2 Simplify each of these, leaving your answer as a single power of a number.

a $2^3 \times 2^4$ **b** $5^6 \times 5^3$ **c** $3^{12} \div 3^4$
d $6^3 \div 6^2$ **e** $a^3 \times a^6$ **f** $b^4 \div b$
g $\dfrac{4^5 \times 4^9}{4^4}$ **h** $\dfrac{5^4 \times 5^{10} \times 5}{5^6}$ **i** $\dfrac{p^4 \times p^4}{p^3}$
j $\dfrac{w^4 \times w}{w}$ **k** $\dfrac{s \times s^3}{s^2}$ **l** $\dfrac{f^5 \times f}{f^5}$

3 Use the divisibility test to answer each of these questions. In each case explain your answer.

a Is 2 a factor of 189?
b Is 5 a factor of 1935?
c Is 11 a factor of 5445?
d Is 3 a factor of 279?
e Are 3 and 5 both factors of 390?
f Are 3 and 11 both factors of 8525?

4 Work out the value of each of these expressions.

a $3^2 \times 4$ **b** $2^4 \times 5^2$ **c** $3 \times 5^3 \times 11$
d $3^2 \times 5 \times 13$ **e** $2 \times 5^3 \times 3$ **f** $2 \times 11^2 \times 13$
g 3×11^4 **h** $5^3 \times 11^2$ **i** $2 \times 3 \times 5 \times 13$

1 Here are some numbers.

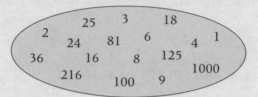

From the numbers inside the oval, write the numbers that are

a prime numbers
b square numbers
c cube numbers
d factors of 24
e prime factors of 18
f factors of both 24 and 36.
g Salma says '6 is a cube number because $2^3 = 6$'. Salma is wrong. Explain why.

2 Work out the value of

a $(3^2)^3$

b $(\sqrt{4})^2$

c $a^2 \times a^4$

d $\dfrac{3^4 \times 3^5}{3}$

e 5^0

3 a Express 72 as a product of its prime factors.
  b Find the highest common factor (HCF) of 72 and 24.

4 1800 can be expressed by the products of prime factors
$2^x \times 3^y \times 5^z$

Find the values of x, y and z.

1 Write down the numbers inside the oval that are

  a odd numbers
  b square numbers
  c cube numbers
  d factors of 18
  e prime factors of 36
  f highest common
     factor of 24 and 18
  g lowest common multiple of 6 and 4.

2   24   144   3   24   1
24   49   6   4
36   16   8   5   1000
216   100   9

2 Which pair of triangles is congruent?

  a i   **ii**  **iii**

  b i   **ii** 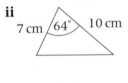 **iii**

3 Solve these equations.

  a $4x + 3 = 23$
  b $15 - 3x = 9$
  c $8(x + 4) = 16$
  d $\dfrac{x}{4} + 5 = 10$
  e $14 + x = 8$
  f $4x - 10 = -26$
  g $4x - 4 = -12$
  h $3(5 - x) = -3$

4 The weights in kg of 30 adults are given.

  57   72   53   76   83   49   59   59   79   88
  73   90   89   57   60   91   69   99   96   81
  70   72   83   52   94   57   74   75   80   77

  Draw an ordered stem-and-leaf diagram to represent this
  information. Choose suitable stems.

1 Substitute the values $a = 2$, $b = 3$, $c = \frac{1}{2}$ into each expression.

  a $4a + b$ **b** $ac + 1$

  c $2b - a$ **d** $6b + c$

  e $2a + b + 5c$ **f** $3c + 2a - b$

  g $(a + b)^2$ **h** $2a^2 - 2c$

  i $\dfrac{bc}{a}$ **j** $3ab + 2bc$

2 a Expand these brackets.

    i $4(x + 5)$ **ii** $5(x + 3)$

    iii $4(3 - x)$ **iv** $3(2x + 4)$

  b Factorise these expressions.

    i $3x + 9$ **ii** $5x - 20$

    iii $12x + 6$ **iv** $4x + 8$

3 The voltage V in an electrical circuit, with current I and resistance R, is given by the formula

  $V = IR$

  a What is V when   **i** $I = 6$ and $R = 8$

                          ii $I = 8$ and $R = 12$?

  b What is R when $V = 56$ and $I = 8$?

4 The formula for the volume V of a cuboid is

  $V = lwh$

  where l = length, w = width and h = height.

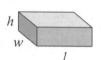

  a Find the volume of a cuboid with $l = 5$ cm, $w = 2$ cm, $h = 3$ cm.

  b Which of these cuboids will give the largest volume?

    i $l = 4$ cm, $w = 5$ cm, $h = 2$ cm

    ii $l = 4$ cm, $w = 3$ cm, $h = 3$ cm

    iii $l = 5$ cm, $w = 1$ cm, $h = 7$ cm

1 Tickets for the cinema cost £4.50 for adults and £2.50 for children.

   a Write a formula for the total cost, C, for p adults and q children.

The total cost of tickets for a group of adults and children to go to the cinema was £25.50.

   b If there were 3 children, work out how many adults went to the cinema.

2 The cost of hiring a cement mixer is £29 plus £5 for each hour.

   a Write a formula for the cost, C, to hire the cement mixer for n hours.

   b Use your formula to work out how much it costs to hire a cement mixer for 8 hours.

   c If the cost of hiring a cement mixer was £54, how many hours was it hired for?

3 Rearrange each formula to make a the subject.

   a $a + 4b = 10$

   b $4a - b = 12$

   c $6b + a = 20$

   d $b = \dfrac{a}{3} + 4$

   e $16 + 3a = 7b$

4 Jim's grandmother's formula for calculating the amount of cooking time, t, needed to roast a turkey is

$$t = 0.5w + 2$$

where w = weight of the turkey.

   a Rearrange the formula to make w the subject.

   b Using the rearranged formula, work out the weight of the turkey if Jim uses a cooking time, t, of

     i   3.5 hours

     ii   3 hours

     iii   5 hours.

1 Whilst doing a science experiment, Sam is told to use the equation

$$v = 9.81t - 5.27$$

to work out the value of v.
She uses her calculator to work out the value of v when $t = 5.89$.

a Work out the correct value of v when $t = 5.89$.
b Rearrange the equation $v = 9.81t - 5.27$ to make t the subject.
c Use the equation in **b** to work out the value of t when $v = 56.0425$.

2 a Expand $x(4x^2 + 3)$
b Simplify $3x^3y \times 4x^2y^2$
c Factorise $5x^3 + 12x$

3 Sonia said, 'When $x = 4$, then the value of $3x^2$ is 48'.
Trevor said, 'When $x = 4$, then the value of $3x^2$ is 144'.

a Who was right?
Explain why.
b Work out the value of $5(x + 3)^3$ when $x = 2$.

4 Emily says:

'For all prime numbers, n, the value of $n^2 + 5$ is always an even number'

Give an example to show that Emily is **not** correct.

1 Use your calculator, where necessary, to work out these.

a 6^2 **b** 14^2 **c** 4^3

d 1^3 **e** 15^2 **f** $(-6)^2$

g 7^3 **h** 12^3 **i** 10^3

j $\sqrt{81}$ **k** $\sqrt{169}$ **l** $\sqrt[3]{64}$

m $\sqrt[3]{17\,576}$ **n** $\sqrt{4900}$ **o** $\sqrt[3]{1000}$

2 Expand the brackets in these expressions and simplify where necessary.

a $3(x+5)$ **b** $4(x-4)$

c $x(x+4)$ **d** $2(2x+5)$

e $-3(x+3)$ **f** $-2x(x+4)$

g $3(x+4)+4(x-4)$ **h** $3(x-4)+6(x-2)$

i $5(x-2)+7(x+3)$

3 Copy the shapes and rotate them through the given angle and direction about the dot.

a   **b**   **c**

270° clockwise   90° anticlockwise   180°

4 The heights, h, of 100 students are recorded.

Height, h, m	Frequency
$1.40 < h \leqslant 1.45$	12
$1.45 < h \leqslant 1.50$	14
$1.50 < h \leqslant 1.55$	27
$1.55 < h \leqslant 1.60$	23
$1.60 < h \leqslant 1.65$	19
$1.65 < h \leqslant 1.70$	5

Draw a frequency polygon to illustrate this information.

1 Calculate the third angle of each of these triangles and state the type of triangle.

   a 35°, 100°   **b** 45°, 90°   **c** 15°, 120°

   d 60°, 60°   **e** 27°, 143°   **f** 75°, 30°

2 The points A (−3, 2) and B (−3, −4) are shown. Give the coordinates of a point C so that triangle ABC is

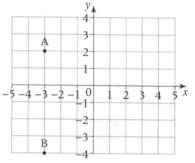

   a isosceles with area 15 square units

   b right-angled scalene with area 9 square units

   c right-angled isosceles with area 18 square units.

3 Plot the points (1, 3) and (3, 1) on a copy of this grid. These points are two vertices (corners) of a shape. Using a different grid for each shape, add other vertices to make a

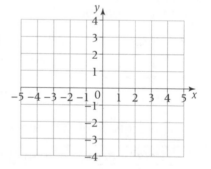

   a square

   b parallelogram

   c trapezium

   d kite.

4 a Copy and complete the table.

Shape	Number of lines of symmetry	Order of rotational symmetry	Description of diagonals
Rectangle			
Parallelogram			
Rhombus			

   b Extend the table to add an isosceles trapezium, square and kite.

1 Draw a sketch of the nets for these shapes.

  a cuboid   **b** cylinder

  c triangular prism   **d** square-based pyramid

2 Which of these is the net for this cube?

3 On squared paper draw

  i the plan   **ii** the front elevation   **iii** the side elevation
of these solids.

  a   **b**   **c**   **d**

  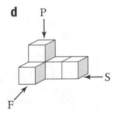

4 The plan and side elevation
of a prism are shown.
The front elevation shows its
cross-section.

  a On squared paper draw a
    side elevation of the prism.

  b Draw a 3-D sketch of the prism.

Front elevation   **Plan**

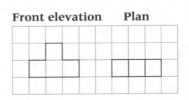

1 This is a 4 by 4 by 4 cube on a set of *x, y, z* axes. One of the vertices is at (0, 0, 0). Write the coordinates of the other 7 vertices.

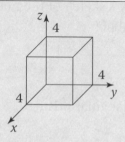

2 The diagram shows a solid object.

  a Sketch the side elevation from the direction marked with an arrow.

  b Sketch the plan of the solid object.

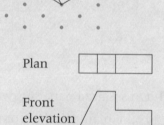

3 Here are the plan and front elevation of a prism. The front elevation shows the cross-section of the prism.

  a On squared paper draw a side elevation of the prism.

  b Draw a 3-D sketch of the prism.

Plan

Front elevation

4 Copy the table. For each of these shapes, put a tick in the box if the statement is always true.

Statement	Square	Rhombus	Trapezium
Diagonals cross at right angles			
Opposite sides are parallel			
Opposite sides are equal			

1 Draw a sketch of the nets for these shapes. Name the shapes.

a

b

2 Rearrange these formulae to make a the subject.

a $a + 3b = 12$

b $2a - 3b = 15$

c $8b + a = 24$

d $b = \dfrac{a}{5} - 5$

e $15 - 3a = 6b$

3 Write these ratios in the form $1 : n$.

a 3 : 12	**b** 4 : 12	**c** 5 : 20
d 14 : 28	**e** 5 : 25	**f** 15 : 45
g 4 : 32	**h** 6 : 36	**i** 24 : 48
j 12 : 18	**k** 24 : 36	**l** 32 : 48

Hint: The ratio can be a fraction or decimal.

4 A recipe for cottage pie to serve 4 people used 600 g of beef. How much beef is needed for a cottage pie to serve

a 1 person **b** 6 people **c** 15 people?

5 A building contractor pays nine workers £1395 for one day's work. How much would he pay

a 5 workers **b** 10 workers **c** 15 workers?

6 There are 14 lb in one stone, and 1 kg is 2.2 lb. How many kg are there in

a 10 stone and 3 lb

b 7 stone and 1 lb

c 19 stone and 9 lb?

1 Copy each of these calculations and insert brackets, where necessary, to make each statement correct. Not every statement needs brackets.

a $4 + 3 \times 4 = 28$ **b** $6 \div 4 - 1 = 2$

c $7 \times 2 + 8 \div 4 = 16$ **d** $3^2 - 4 \times 2 + 6 = 40$

e $60 \times 2^2 - 1 = 180$ **f** $3 + 2 \times 9 = 45$

g $5 + 20 \div 4 = 10$ **h** $4^2 + 3 \times 2 = 38$

i $3 \times 2 + 4 \times 6 = 30$

2 Work out these calculations.

a $5 + 4 \times 5$ **b** $10 + 2 \times 6 + 3$

c $4 + 2 \times (4 + 5)$ **d** $4^2 - 10 \div 2$

e $12 \div 3 - 2 \times 2$ **f** $(5 + 16) \div 3$

g $8 + 4^3 \times 2$ **h** $3 \times (5 - 3) + 1$

i $80 \div 2^3 + 3 \times 8$ **j** $\dfrac{6 + 4 \times 4}{11}$

k $\dfrac{4 \times 5 + 2}{2}$ **l** $\dfrac{81}{2^2 + 5}$

Example

Work out these mentally.   **a** 16×0.2 **b** $24 \div 0.02$

a $16 \times 0.2 = 16 \times 2 \times 0.1 = 32 \times 0.1 = 3.2$

b $24 \div 0.02 = 24 \div 2 \div 0.01 = 12 \div 0.01 = 1200$

3 Work out these calculations using a mental method. Show your method.

a 4×0.02 **b** $32 \div 0.8$ **c** 1.6×0.4

d $6 \div 0.03$ **e** $2.1 \div 0.07$

4 Write a suitable estimate for each of these calculations. In each case clearly show how you estimated your answer.

a $\dfrac{39.9 \times 21.5}{1.98^3}$ **b** $\dfrac{47.9 \times 9.8^2}{0.49 \times 21.56}$ **c** $\sqrt{98.7 \div 1.98}$

d $\{2.6^2 + (4.57 - 0.62)\}^2$ **e** $\dfrac{219 + (3.98 + 16.08)^2}{\sqrt{74.5 \div 2.11}}$

1 **a** Using the information that $12 \times 465 = 5580$ write the value of

    i 1.2×465 **ii** 12×4.65 **iii** $5580 \div 1.2$

  b Using the information that $46 \times 298 = 13\,708$ write the value of

    i 0.46×29.8 **ii** $13\,708 \div 0.46$ **iii** $1370.8 \div 4.6$

  c Using the information that $89 \times 245 = 21\,805$ write the value of

    i $21.805 \div 89$ **ii** 8.9×0.245 **iii** 8900×0.245

2 Use an approximate mental method to work out each of these problems.

  a Sam sends 89 text messages at 9.8p a text. How much does it cost her in total?

  b A cube has sides of length 4.9 cm. What is its volume?

  c Michelle talks to her friend on the phone for 18.5 minutes. It costs 15.9p a minute. How much does the phone call cost?

  d A shop sells these items:

    Work out the cost of

Strawberries	**£1.89** a box
Cherries	**£2.99** a bag
Grapes	**£1.87** a kg

    i 3 boxes of strawberries

    ii 2 bags of cherries and 2 kg of grapes

    iii 1 box of strawberries, 3 bags of cherries and 3 kg of grapes.

3 Use an appropriate method of calculation to work out

  a 16×43 **b** 15×54 **c** 23×466

  d $184 \div 4$ **e** $203 \div 7$ **f** $375 \div 15$

  g 7.6×4 **h** 17×6.5 **i** 1.74×13

  j $32.76 \div 9.1$ **k** $59.52 \div 6.4$ **l** $99.54 \div 7.9$

4 Steve is an electrician and he charges £49.50 as a call out charge and then £22.25 for each hour he works. How much does he get for 3.5 hours work?

1 Work out these calculations.

   a 3.56×6.5 **b** $20.05 \div 3.5$ **c** 12.11×2.4

2 **a** Use your calculator to work out the value of $\dfrac{3.45 \times 6.79}{3.67 + 5.97}$

    Write all of the figures shown on your calculator display.

  b Write your answer to part **a** to an appropriate degree of accuracy.

3 Sanjay mends computers.
He charges
   £46.80 for the first hour on a computer and
   £32.50 for each extra hour's work.
Sanjay repaired a computer and charged a total of £241.80.
Without using a calculator and showing all of your workings, work out how many hours it took Sanjay to mend the computer.

4 Whilst doing a science experiment, Michelle is told to use the equation

   $v = 9.91t + 5.45$

to work out the value of v.
She uses her calculator to work out the value of v when $t = 6.78$

  a Work out the correct value of v when $t = 6.78$.

When $t = 8.26$ Michelle works out the answer to be 87.3066.
Michelle's answer is correct.
Michelle's friend Leah worked out v to be 23.62 when $t = 8.26$.

  b Explain fully what is the most likely error made by Leah.

1 Calculate the area and perimeter of these shapes.

a

b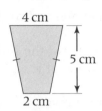

c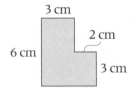

d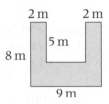

2 For each of these give a suitable estimate.
Show your workings clearly.

a 9.74×4.98

b $92.7 \div 6.12$

c $\dfrac{12.94 \times 9.94}{5.87}$

d $\dfrac{78.9 \times 29.99}{25.4}$

3 A rectangle has length 15 cm and width x cm.

a Write a formula for the area of the rectangle.
b Use an equation to determine x if the area is 135 cm^2.
c Write a formula for the perimeter of the rectangle.
d Use an equation to determine x if the perimeter is 78 cm.

4 The table show the heights and weights of 15 men on a rugby team.

Height in m	1.78	1.85	1.69	1.92	1.88	1.83	1.79	1.95	1.80	1.65	1.77	1.98	1.69	1.90	1.95
Weight in kg	79	85	72	84	82	75	79	80	81	76	74	86	70	85	86

a Plot the points on a scatter diagram.
b Describe in words the relationship between the height and weight of the men.
c State the type of correlation shown in this graph.

1 The diagram shows a square with sides $4y + 3$.

   a Write an expression for the perimeter of the square.

   b The perimeter of the square is 108 cm. Find the value of y.

$4y + 3$

2 The diagram shows a rectangle of side lengths $2x - 3$ and 5.

   a Write an expression for the area of the rectangle.

   b The area of the rectangle is 45 cm². Find the value of x.

5

$2x - 3$

3 Solve these equations.

   a $3(x + 5) = 24$ **b** $5(x - 2) = 35$

   c $4(10 - x) = 28$ **d** $-2(x + 5) = -20$

   e $4(x + 4) = 8$ **f** $7(2x + 4) = 4$

   g $3x + 2 = 6x - 2$ **h** $5x - 3 = 3x + 3$

   i $9x + 4 = 12x - 11$ **j** $3x + 7 = 5x + 4$

   k $7x - 4 = 3x - 21$ **l** $2x - 4 = 5x + 3.5$

4 Write equations for these 'think of a number' problems and then solve each equation.

   a I think of a number, then multiply it by 5 and add 6. The answer is 21.

   b I think of a number, then multiply it by 4 and add 3. The answer is the same as multiplying the same number by 5 and subtracting 2.

   c I think of a number and add 6, then multiply it by 4 and the answer is 36.

   d I think of a number, then multiply it by 7 and subtract 5. The answer is the same as multiplying the same number by 3 and adding 3.

   e I think of a number and subtract 5, then multiply by 4 and the answer is -32.

1 Solve these equations.

a $2(b + 1) = 3b - 22$ **b** $5(f - 2) = 4(f + 1)$
c $2(k + 1) = 3k - 41$ **d** $4(u - 2) = 2(u + 10)$
e $4(v + 1) = 6v - 44$ **f** $3(x + 5) = 2x + 19$
g $5y - 10 = -4(y + 7)$ **h** $5(2x + 4) = 5(4x + 1)$

2 Solve these equations.

a $\dfrac{x + 3}{2} = 4$ **b** $\dfrac{x + 3}{5} = 4$

c $\dfrac{3x - 6}{2} = 4.5$ **d** $\dfrac{3x - 6}{6} = 4.5$

e $\dfrac{10 - x}{2} = 3$ **f** $\dfrac{12 - 2x}{2} = 1$

g $\dfrac{3x + 2}{2} = 4$ **h** $\dfrac{5x + 2}{2} = -2$

i $\dfrac{3x - 4}{13} = 2$ **j** $\dfrac{5 - 3x}{7} = 2$

3 In the two-way flow diagrams, find the starting number y that has to be input, so that you reach the same finish number F whichever route is followed. Formulate an equation to solve. The first one has been started.

a 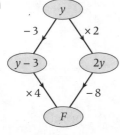   **b** 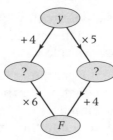   **c**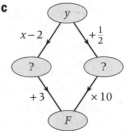

4 Write two different equations that have a solution of $x = 3$. You should write one question similar to question **1** and another similar to question **2**. Show your solutions.

1 The equation $2x^2 + 3x = 21$
has a solution between 2 and 3.
Use trial and improvement to find the solution to
1 decimal place.

Hint: Create a table to help you.

2 The equation $x^3 + 4x = 198$
has a solution between 5 and 6.
Use trial and improvement to find this solution.
Give your answer correct to one decimal place.
You must show **all** your working.

3 A cuboid has a square base of side length y cm.
The height of the cuboid is 2 cm more than y cm.
The volume of the cuboid is 34 cm^3.

a Show that $y^3 + 2y^2 = 34$.

The equation $y^3 + 2y^2 = 34$ has a solution between $y = 2$
and $y = 3$.

b Use trial and improvement to find this solution.
Give your answer correct to 1 decimal place.
You must show **all** your working.

4 This is a garden in the shape of a
rectangle.
All measurements are in metres.
The garden has a pond in one corner.
The pond is a square of side x.

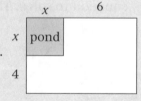

a The perimeter of the garden is 32
metres. Write an equation for the
perimeter of the garden.

b Solve the equation to find the size of the pond.

1 Write down the names of these 2-D and 3-D shapes.

a   b   c   d   e

f   g   h   i   j

2 Draw the nets for shapes *b*, *d*, *e*, *f* and *i* in question **1**.

3 Use a written method to work these out.

  a 17×25 **b** 24×16 **c** 45×347

  d $318 \div 6$ **e** $504 \div 9$ **f** $208 \div 16$

  g 7.6×6 **h** 17×7.5 **i** 3.74×18

  j $112.5 \div 9$ **k** $63.6 \div 12$ **l** $29.25 \div 9$

4 A bag contains 5 grey balls, 2 white balls and 3 black balls.

One ball is taken out of the bag and then replaced.
Calculate the probability that the ball is

  a white

  b black

  c grey

  d red.

  e If you were to take out a ball and then replace it 200 times, how many times would you expect to get a white ball?

1 Calculate the range for each set of numbers.

   a 7, 8, 12, 4, 3

   b 1, 1, 3, 4, 4, 4, 5, 5, 5, 7, 7, 8

   c 0.45, 0.38, 0.12, 0.5, 0.75, 0.8

   d 32, 35, 33, 26, 37, 54, 23, 26

   e $1\frac{1}{2}$, 3, $4\frac{1}{4}$, 5, $3\frac{1}{4}$, 4, 5, 3, $4\frac{3}{4}$, 5

   f £3.45, £8.45, £0.45, £9.03, £4.59, £3.99

2 The heights of students in a class, in metres, are

1.60	1.45	1.51	1.63	1.70	1.46	1.38	1.44
1.52	1.39	1.50	1.48	1.60	1.52	1.36	1.70
1.63	1.55	1.49	1.36	1.45	1.42	1.51	1.67

   a Are these discrete or continuous data?

   b Calculate the range of the heights.

3 Calculate the **i** mode, **ii** median, **iii** mean of each set of numbers.

   a 1, 4, 4, 4, 4, 5, 6

   b 0, 0, 3, 2, 5, 12, 4, 4, 6

   c 3, 4, 5, 5, 4, 2, 6, 7

   d 15, 16, 12, 13, 16, 12

   e 2.4, 1.5, 2.5, 1.7, 2.8, 2.3, 1.5, 1.3

Example

Work out the missing number if the mean of these four numbers is 12.

   10   8   16 x

$10 + 8 + 16 + x = 12 \times 4 = 48$

$34 + x = 48$

$x = 14$

---

4 Work out the missing numbers in each set.

   a The mean of these six numbers is 10.

      5   8   14   12   9   ?

   b The mean of these five numbers is 10 and the mode is 9.

      10   9   14   ?   ?

   c The mean of these six numbers is 7, the median is 7 and the range is 9.

      10   1   8   6   ?   ?

1 The number of brothers and sisters 13 students have are recorded in the table.

No. of brothers and sisters	0	1	2	3	4	5
No. of students	1	3	5	1	2	1

   a Calculate the mean, median, mode number of brothers and sisters.

   b Calculate the range in number of brothers and sisters.

2 Students in a class took a mental arithmetic test. The results are shown in the table.

Marks in test	4	5	6	7	8	9
No. of students	2	1	5	8	12	4

Calculate the mean, median, mode and range for the test results.

3 The number of goals scored by two teams over 10 games were

Team A

Number of goals	Frequency
0	3
1	4
2	1
3	1
4	1

Team B

Number of goals	Frequency
0	1
1	4
2	5
3	0
4	0

   a Calculate the mean, median, mode and range for each team.

   b By comparing your calculations in part **a**, what can you say about the number of goals scored by each team?

4 In an English test the boys' mean score was 56% and range was 12%. The girls' mean score was 62% and range was 23%. What can you say about the performance of boys compared to girls?

1 Some students took a mental arithmetic test. Their marks are shown in the frequency table.

Mark	Frequency
5	1
6	2
7	3
8	10
9	14
10	1

a Work out how many students took the test.

b Write the modal mark.

25 students had a higher mark than Sharon.

c Work out Sharon's mark.

d Find the median mark.

e Work out the range of the marks.

2 Chris asked 50 people how much they paid for a new computer.
The results are shown in this frequency table.

Price P in £	Number of computers
$0 < P \leqslant 500$	2
$500 < P \leqslant 1000$	15
$1000 < P \leqslant 1500$	14
$1500 < P \leqslant 2000$	10
$2000 < P \leqslant 2500$	9

Calculate an estimate for the mean price paid for a new computer.

3 Mrs Ingram gives her class a Maths test.
Here are the test marks for the girls.

7, 5, 8, 5, 2, 8, 7, 4, 7, 10, 3, 7, 4, 3, 6

a Work out the mode.   **b** Work out the median.

The boys' median mark was 7 and the boys' range of marks was 4. The range of the girls' marks was 8.

c By comparing the results explain whether the boys or girls did better in the test.

1 The diagram shows a solid object.

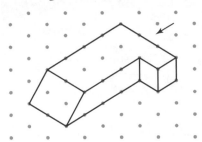

   a Sketch the side elevation from the direction marked with an arrow.

   b Sketch the plan of the solid object.

2 Jade and Laura sell bags of treats at dog shows. The table shows how much profit they made at 30 shows.

Profit, P, £	Number of bags
$0 < P \leqslant 500$	4
$500 < P \leqslant 1000$	7
$1000 < P \leqslant 1500$	9
$1500 < P \leqslant 2000$	7
$2000 < P \leqslant 2500$	3

Calculate an estimate for the mean profit over 30 dog shows.

3 **a** A square has an area of 529 cm^2. What is the length of the square?

   b A cube has a volume of 1728 cm^3. What are its dimensions?

   c Between which two whole numbers does $\sqrt{60}$ lie? Explain your answer.

4 Solve these equations.

   a $\dfrac{x+4}{3} = 21$ **b** $3(5x - 6) = 147$ **c** $\dfrac{2(x+6)}{3} = 6$

   d $2x + 4 = 3x - 1$ **e** $6(x + 1) = 14(x - 1)$ **f** $2(5x + 3) = 12x - 3$

1 A castle and church are on a small island.
A treasure chest is buried on the island.
The bearing of the treasure from the castle is 95°.
The bearing of the treasure from the church is 190°.
Copy the diagram of the island above and mark the position of the treasure.

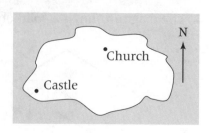

2 Measure the bearing of

  a Coventry from Birmingham
  b Worcester from Birmingham
  c Birmingham from Coventry
  d Worcester from Coventry.

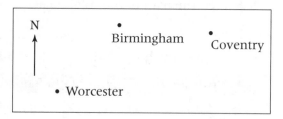

3 Make accurate drawings of these triangles.

  a SAS   **b** ASA   **c** SSS

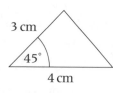

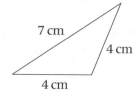

4 Make an accurate drawing of this net of a square-based pyramid.

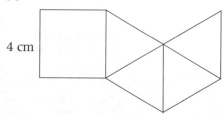

1 a Draw a line AB, so that AB = 12 cm.

A ————————•———————— B
            P

b Mark the point P, so that AP = 8 cm.

c Construct the perpendicular to AB that passes through point P.

2 a Using a compass construct the triangle ABC.

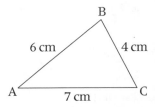

b Construct the perpendicular bisectors of AB, BC and AC.

c Label the point of intersection of the perpendicular bisectors as O.

d What do you notice about point O?

3 Construct an equilateral triangle of side length 5 cm using only a ruler and compasses. You must show your construction lines.

4 a Using compasses, construct the triangle PQR.

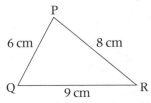

b Construct the angle bisectors for the angle P, angle Q and angle R.

c Label the point of intersection as O.

d Draw a circle, centre O, that just touches the lines PQ, QR and PR.

e State the radius of this circle.

1 Construct an accurate drawing of this triangle.

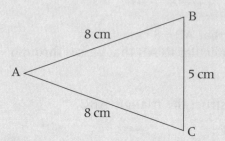

2 The triangle in question **1** represents a triangular garden ABC.
The scale of the diagram is 1 cm = 1 m.
A pond is to be built in the garden so that it is
i within 4 m of point C
ii equal distance from AB and AC.
On your triangle that you constructed in question **1**, use a cross to show the possible location of the pond.

3 Copy the line AB and draw the locus of the points that are always 2 cm from the line.

4 Make an accurate copy of the points A, B and C.
(You can use tracing paper.)

A .

· C

B ·

Shade the region that satisfies all three of these conditions

a Less than 2 cm from A
b Closer to AB than to AC
c Closer to A than to B.

1 In the equation
$$2x^2 + 3x = 78$$
x is between 5 and 6.
Use the trial and improvement method to find x.
Give your answer correct to one decimal place.
You must show **all** your workings.

2 The number of goals scored by a team in 40 games are

3 4 5 2 4 4 3 0 1 4 3 4 0 1 2 1 3 3 5 0
4 0 2 2 5 3 0 4 2 2 1 0 0 3 4 1 1 2 3 4

a Draw a frequency table for these results.
b Calculate the mean, median, mode and range of the goals.

3 Here are the plan and side elevation of a prism.
The side elevation shows the cross section of the prism.

Plan

Side elevation

a On square paper, draw the front elevation of the prism.
b Draw a 3-D sketch of the prism.

4 Mr Collins gave his English class a spelling test.
Here are the test marks for the girls.
9 10 4 7 8 8 6 9 10 9 10 7 10

a Find the mode.   **b** Find the median.

The median mark for the boys was 7 and the range of the
boys' marks was 4. The range of the girls' marks was 6.

c By comparing the results, explain whether the boys or
girls did better in the test.

1 Use a suitable method to calculate

a $\frac{3}{11}$ of £33 **b** $\frac{5}{7}$ of 350 kg **c** $\frac{7}{9}$ of 63p

d $\frac{11}{20}$ of 100 g **e** $\frac{9}{15}$ of 45° **f** $\frac{14}{25}$ of €600

g $\frac{5}{6}$ of $300 **h** $\frac{6}{13}$ of £104 **i** $\frac{1}{6}$ of 192 people

j $\frac{1}{20}$ of 500 people **k** $\frac{7}{12}$ of 168 cm **l** $\frac{9}{11}$ of 572 miles

2 Express each of these as proportions. Give your answer as a fraction in its simplest form.

a 50 kg as a fraction of 80 kg
b £20 as a proportion of £50
c 16 cm as a fraction of 64 cm
d 450 cm as a fraction of 600 cm
e 44 minutes as a proportion of 60 minutes
f 540 metres as a fraction of 4 metres
g 78p as a fraction of £2.

3 **a** Find these percentages without using a calculator. You must show all of your workings.

i 50% of £400 **ii** 25% of £200
iii 10% of £60 **iv** 1% of 600p
v 30% of €550 **vi** 20% of $350
vii 40% of 90p **viii** 15% of $800
ix 55% of 1800 g **x** 75% of 860 kg
xi 35% of €180 **xii** 13% of 40 cm

b Use a suitable method to calculate these. Where appropriate round your answers to 2 decimal places.

i 25% of £49 **ii** 17.5% of 67 m
iii 34% of $458 **iv** 12% of 740 tonnes
v 98% of 58 kg **vi** 89% of 2550 mm
vii 135% of 135 km **viii** 7% of 95 m

4 A 500 ml smoothie drink is made up of these juices
33% strawberry 21% banana 22% orange
11% grape 13% apple
Calculate the number of ml of each type of juice.

1 a Find these without using a calculator.

    i Increase £40 by 10%   **ii** Decrease 160 m by 20%
    iii Decrease £86 by 15%   **iv** Increase 740 kg by 35%
    v Increase £48 by 17.5%   **vi** Decrease 480p by 1%

  b Calculate these giving your answers correct to 2 decimal places.

    i Increase £97 by 12%   **ii** Decrease $78 by 27%
    iii Decrease 89 kg by 58%   **iv** Increase 270 g by 86%
    v Increase $890 by 17%   **vi** Decrease 1350 m by 83%

2 Use an appropriate method to work out each of these problems. Give your answer to 2 decimal places where necessary.

  a A holiday cost £495 but it is reduced by 15% in a sale. Calculate the new price of the holiday.

  b Mr Holmes earns £456 a week. He has a pay increase of 3%. Work out how much he will earn after the pay increase.

  c A plumber charges Teresa £4389 for new central heating. If the bill is paid within 7 days he reduces the bill by 5%. Teresa pays within 7 days. Work out how much she saves.

3 Copy and complete the table.

Item	Cost price	% increase or decrease	Selling price
TV	£499	17.5% increase	
Microwave	£89.50	10% decrease	
Cooker	£245.50	20% increase	
Fridge	£389	2.5% decrease	

4 a A shop buys cakes for 50p each and sells them for 89p. What is the percentage profit?

  b Paul buys a car for £3995 and sells it one year later for £3125. Work out the percentage loss.

1 Ayesha put £564 in a new savings account.
Simple interest of 4% was added to the amount in her savings each year.

Calculate the total amount in Ayesha's savings account at the end of 2 years.

2 Fred pays Income Tax at 22%.
He is allowed to earn £3500 before he pays any Income Tax. He earns £14 500 in one year.

Work out how much Income Tax he pays in that year.

3 £600 is invested for 2 years at 6% per annum compound interest.

a Work out the total interest earned over the 2 years.

£250 is invested for 3 years at 7% per annum compound interest.

b Work out the total amount at the end of the 3 years.

4 Water is stored in a tank in the shape of a cuboid with a square base.
The sides of the base are 30 cm long.
The depth of the water is 20 cm.

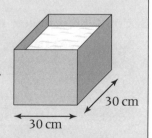

30 cm

30 cm

a Work out the volume of the water, in cm³.

More water is put in the tank. The depth of the water rises to 21.6 cm.

b Calculate the percentage increase in the volume of water in the tank.

1 This map shows the position of several cities and towns.

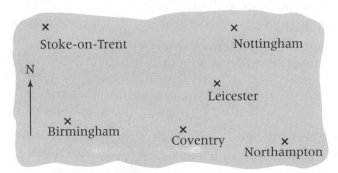

Measure and write down the bearing of

a Coventry from Birmingham
b Northampton from Coventry
c Stoke-on-Trent from Nottingham
d Leicester from Northampton

2 Calculate these percentage increases or decreases without using a calculator.
You must show all of your working.

a Increase £250 by 10%   **b** Decrease £400 by 25%
c Decrease £60 by 17.5%   **d** Increase 60p by 1%
e Increase €300 by 15%   **f** Decrease $320 by 35%
g Decrease 80p by 65%   **h** Increase $120 by 99%

3 Four numbers have a mean of 5, a median of 5, and a mode of 5, but have a range of 4.
What could these four numbers be?

4 Work out the value of each expression.

a $6d + 4f$ when $d = 5$ and $f = 4$
b $7m + n$ when $m = 4$ and $n = -5$
c $7p - 3q$ when $p = 15$ and $q = -1$
d $9e - d + 2f$ when $e = 4$, $d = -2$ and $f = \frac{1}{2}$

1 The pie chart shows the favourite foods for 60 students. Calculate

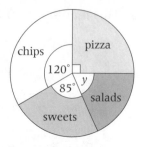

  a the value of y
  b the angle that represents 1 student
  c the number of students who like

  i pizza **ii** chips
  iii salads **iv** sweets.

2 The number of books 42 students read in 1 month is recorded in a pictogram.

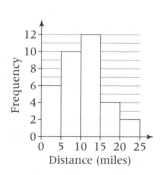

  a What does ☐│☐ represent?
  b Calculate the mean number of books read.
  c Calculate the proportion of students that read 2 or more books a month.

3 The histogram shows the distances people drive to work in miles.

  a How many people travel between

  i 0 and 5 miles
  ii 15 and 20 miles to work?

  b What is the modal class interval?
  c Calculate the total number of people in the survey.

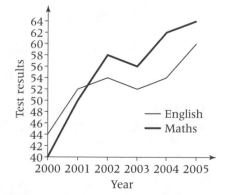

4 The Key Stage 3 Maths and English results for six years are represented by these frequency polygons. Make two statements about the Maths and English KS3 test results over the 6 years.

1 The heights, in m, of 18 students in a class are recorded.

1.67   1.72   1.80   1.59   1.60   1.64   1.74   1.81   1.52
1.56   1.73   1.83   1.89   1.76   1.65   1.69   1.76   1.77

  a Copy and complete an ordered stem-and-leaf diagram.

    15 | Key: 16 | 7 means 1.67 m
    16 |
    17 |
    18 |

  b Calculate the **i** mean **ii** mode **iii** median **iv** range.

2 The stem-and-leaf diagrams for pulse rates in beats per minute (bpm) before and after gentle exercise are

Before exercise		**After exercise**	
4	1	4	Key: 4	1 means 41 bpm
5	1 2 2 5	5	
6	4 5 5 6 8	6	7
7	0 1 1 2 2 4 6 8 8	7	3 7 9
8	1 4	8	2 4 8 8
9	0	9	2 2 3 4 5 7 9 9
10		10	2 4 6 7
11		11	0 1

  a Calculate the median and range for both diagrams.
  b Make two comparisons between the pulse rate before and after exercise.

3 The line graph shows a liquid cooling over 30 minutes, after being heated to 100 °C.

  a What is the temperature after

    i 5 minutes
    ii 25 minutes?

  b Calculate the overall decrease in temperature over 30 minutes.

  c At what time had the temperature decreased by 25%?

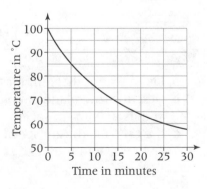

1 The table shows the heights in m, and weights in kg, of 10 footballers.

Height	1.73	1.65	1.79	1.75	1.84	1.81	1.89	1.76	1.80	1.84
Weight	73	63	82	70	83	79	91	74	84	86

   a Draw a scatter diagram to show these data on suitable axes.
   b State the type of correlation between height and weight of the football players.
   c Draw a line of best fit.
   d Use your line of best fit to estimate a footballer's

      i height if their weight is 75 kg
      ii weight if their height is 1.69 m.

2 The manager at 'Wash and Drive' records the time, to the nearest minute, to wash 20 cars. Here are the results

   15 22 9 16 18 27 22 31 10 30
   28 27 19 11 27 22 24 27 19 17

   a Draw a stem-and-leaf diagram to show this information.
   b Work out the median time used to wash a car.
   c The manager gives his workers a target of all cars must be washed in 22 minutes. Do you think this is a fair target? Explain your answer.

3 The table shows the engine size and maximum speed of 10 cars.

Maximum speed (mph)	100	94	84	113	131	135	135	107	142	134
Engine size (cc)	1300	1100	1000	1600	2000	2700	2800	1400	2900	2500

   a Plot a scatter diagram for these data on suitable axes.
   b Describe the relationship between the car's engine size and its maximum speed.
   c If a car's maximum speed is 115 mph, estimate its engine size to the nearest 100.

1 Construct accurate drawings of these triangles.
Use a ruler to measure the unknown lengths in each
triangle.

a 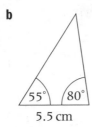   b   c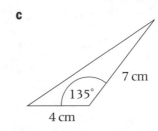

2 a Gemma invests £100 in a bank account.
Simple interest of 4% is added at the end of each year.
Work out how much money Gemma has at the end of

   i the first year
   ii three years.

  b James invests £80 in a bank account.
Compound interest of 3% is added at the end of each year.
Work out how much money James has at the end of

   i the first year
   ii three years.

3 Using algebra, write and solve these equations.

  a a number multiplied by 5 then 6 added equals 36
  b a number subtracted from 9 equals −3
  c 27 is equal to a number multiplied by 4 and 3 added.

4 The times it took 32 students to swim 100 metres are listed.
Times are given in seconds.

298	202	246	287	291	298	279	245
265	278	297	257	234	267	278	276
267	255	246	267	287	299	247	222
227	278	263	260	281	290	214	256

  a Draw a stem-and-leaf diagram to represent this
information.
  b Work out the median time to swim 100 metres.

1 Calculate the surface area of these shapes.
State the units of your answers.

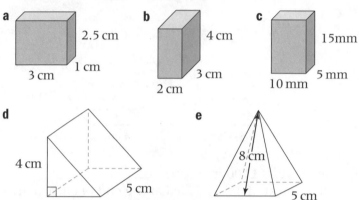

a 2.5 cm 1 cm 3 cm

b 4 cm 3 cm 2 cm

c 15 mm 5 mm 10 mm

d 4 cm 5 cm 3 cm

e 8 cm 5 cm 5 cm

2 A cylinder of height 15 cm is shown.
The diameter of the circle is 6 cm.
Calculate
a the area of the circle
b the surface area of the cylinder.

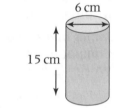

6 cm

15 cm

3 Calculate the volume of the cuboids in
question **1a**, **b** and **c**.

4 Using this formula work out the volume of the shapes.

Volume of prism = Area of cross-section × length

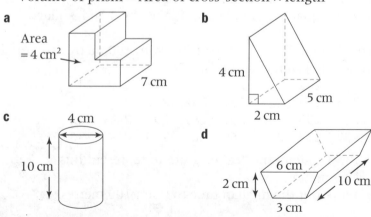

a Area = 4 cm² 7 cm

b 4 cm 2 cm 5 cm

c 4 cm 10 cm

d 6 cm 2 cm 3 cm 10 cm

1 Convert these areas to the given units.

   a 5 cm^2 in mm^2 **b** 500 mm^2 in cm^2

   c $50\,000 \text{ m}^2$ in km^2 **d** 7 m^2 in cm^2

   e $7\,000\,000 \text{ m}^2$ in km^2 **f** 7 km^2 in m^2

   g 4.5 cm^2 in mm^2 **h** 950 mm^2 in cm^2

   i 4000 cm^2 in m^2 **j** 5.25 m^2 in cm^2

   k $1\,200\,000 \text{ m}^2$ in km^2 **l** 1.3 km^2 in m^2

2 a Convert these volumes to litres using $1 \text{ m}^3 = 1000$ litres.

    i 2 m^3 **ii** 8 m^3

    iii 6.7 m^3 **iv** 0.2 m^3

   b Convert these litres back to volumes in m^3.

    i 3500 litres   **ii** 250 litres

    iii 20 000 litres   **iv** 50 litres

3 Copy and complete the table, using the appropriate units.

	Distance	Time	Speed
a	48 metres	8 seconds	
b	360 km		60 km/h
c		0.75 hours	16 mph
d	15 000 metres	0.3 hours	
e		2.5 hours	0.1 mph

Hint: $\text{Speed} = \dfrac{\text{Distance}}{\text{Time}}$

4 Copy and complete the table, using the appropriate units.

	Mass	Volume	Density
a	10 800 g	1000 cm³	
b	2 kg		2 kg/m³
c		500 cm³	0.017 g/cm³
d	4.5 kg		0.225 kg/m³
e	0.3 g	225 mm³	

Hint: $\text{Density} = \dfrac{\text{Mass}}{\text{Volume}}$

1 The table shows some expressions.
The letters a, b and c represent lengths.
Copy the table and tick the columns for each expression
to show whether it can be used to represent a length, an
area, a volume or none of these.

Expression	Length	Area	Volume	None of these
$a + b + c$				
abc				
$ab + bc$				
a^2bc				

2 The table shows some expressions.
The lengths p, q and r represent lengths.
π and 2 are numbers and have no dimensions.
Copy the table and tick the boxes to show which
expressions could represent areas.

$2\pi r$	$2(p^2 + q^2)$	$\pi(r + p)$	πpqr	πr^2	$\dfrac{\pi pqr}{p}$	$2\pi pr$

3 A cube has a surface area of 72 cm².
Work out the volume of the cube.

4 The diagram shows a solid cylinder with
a height of 12 cm and radius 5 cm.

   a Calculate the volume of the cylinder.
      Give your answer correct to 3
      significant figures.

   b The cylinder is made out of aluminium
      which has a density of 2.7 g/cm³.
      Work out the mass of the cylinder.
      Give your answer to 1 decimal place.

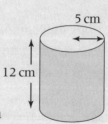

5 cm

12 cm

1 Calculate the volume and surface area of each cuboid.
State the units in your answer.

a 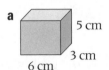 5 cm
3 cm
6 cm

b 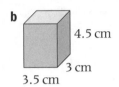 4.5 cm
3 cm
3.5 cm

c 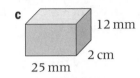 12 mm
2 cm
25 mm

2 The pie chart shows the favourite
film types of 144 students.
Calculate

a the size of the angle for Thriller
b the angle for Comedy
c the angle measure that
   represents one student
d the number of students who
   like

   i Thriller   **ii** Comedy
   iii Romance   **iv** Sci-fi

3 Round these numbers to the given degree of accuracy.

a 46.456   (1 decimal place)
b 67.945   (2 decimal places)
c 356.4589   (3 decimal places)
d 13.96   (1 decimal place)
e 34.5683   (2 decimal places)
f 13.998   (2 decimal places)

4 Convert these areas to the given units.

a $6 \text{ cm}^2 = $ ___ mm^2 b $900 \text{ mm}^2 = $ ___ cm^2
c $60\,000 \text{ mm}^2 = $ ___ m^2 d $10 \text{ m}^2 = $ ___ cm^2
e $9\,000\,000 \text{ m}^2 = $ ___ km^2 f $6 \text{ km}^2 = $ ___ m^2

1 Draw the graphs of these functions, each on a separate grid with axes from +10 to −10.

a $y = 2x + 4$ **b** $y = 5x - 4$

c $x + y = 5$ **d** $4x - y = 5$

2 a Draw the graphs of these functions on the same grid with axes from +10 to −10.

i $y = 3x + 1$ **ii** $y = 3x - 1$

iii $y = 3x$ **iv** $y = 3x + 4$

What do you notice?

b Draw the graphs of these functions on the same grid with axes from +10 to −10.

i $y = -2x + 4$ **ii** $y = -2x$

iii $y = -2x + 5$ **iv** $y = -2x - 4$

What do you notice?

3 a Rearrange these equations into the form $y = mx + c$.

i $2x + y = 6$ **ii** $3y - 6x = -9$

iii $10y + 5x = 40$ **iv** $2y - 4x = -10$

b Write the equation of the line parallel to line $y = 2x + 6$.

4 Write the equations of these lines in order of steepness, starting with the least steep.

a $y = 3x + 4$ **b** $2x - y = 10$

c $y = 4x + 5$ **d** $6y - 3x = 12$

e $4y + x = 20$ **f** $y = \frac{3}{4}x - 2$

g $y - 10x = 5$ **h** $5x - 4y = 20$

1 **a** Draw the graph of $y = -2x - 3$ on a grid with axes from +10 to −10.

   b Use your graph to find

   i the value of x when $y = 9$
   ii the value of y when $x = -2$
   iii the value of x when $y = 0$
   iv the value of y when $x = 3$.

2 **a** Draw the graph of $2y + 4x = -10$ on a grid with axes from +10 to −10.

   b Which of these sets of points lie on the line $2y + 4x = -10$?

(5, −5)	(0, −5)	(−5, 0)
(−6, 7)	(7, −6)	(3, −1)
(−3, 1)	(1, 3)	(−1, −3)
(1, −7)	(−5, 5)	(−5, −5)

3 **a** Draw the graphs of the equations $x + 3y = 6$ and $4x + y = -9$ on the same grid with axes from +10 to −10.

   b Write the coordinates of the point where these two lines cross.

4 **a** Draw the graphs of the equations $2y = x + 9$ and $3y + 4x = 8$ on the same grid with axes from +10 to −10.

   b Write the coordinates of the point where the two lines cross.

1 Here are the equations of five straight lines.
They are labelled from A to E. Copy the table and put a tick to show the lines that are parallel.

A	$2y - x = 6$	
B	$y - 3x = 5$	
C	$2y = 6x + 12$	
D	$y + 1 = 3x$	
E	$6x + 1 = 2y$	

2 Draw the graphs of the equations $2x - 3y = 11$ and $5x + 2y = 18$ on the same grid with axes from +10 to −10. Use your graphs to find solutions to the two equations.

3 a Copy and complete the table of values for $y = 3x - 2$.
b On a suitable grid, draw the graph of $y = 3x - 2$.

x	−3	−2	−1	0	1	2	3
y							

c Use your graph to find

　i　the value of y when $x = -1.5$

　ii　the value of x when $y = 5.5$.

4 Match these graphs to their equations.

　a $y = 2x + 4$
　b $y = x^2$
　c $y = -3$
　d $y = x^2 - 4$
　e $y = -x + 3$
　f $y = -2x + 3$

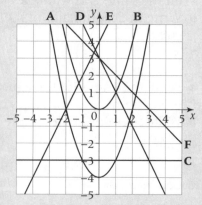

1 Using this formula work out the volume of each shape.
Volume of a prism = Area of cross-section × length

a

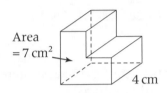

Area
= 7 cm²

4 cm

b

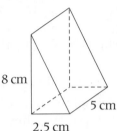

8 cm

5 cm

2.5 cm

2 Write the equations of these lines in order of steepness,
starting with the least steep.

a $y = 4x + 2$

b $3x - y = 10$

c $y = \frac{1}{2}x + 5$

d $6y - 2x = 12$

e $3y - x = 20$

f $y = \frac{3}{4}x - 4$

g $y - 8x = 5$

h $15x - 10y = 20$

3 Claire does a statistical experiment and rolls
a dice 120 times. The dice lands on the six
24 times. Would you say the dice was fair?
Explain your answer.

4 Calculate these, leaving your answers as fractions in their
simplest form where necessary.

a What is the total weight of 9 shopping bags each weighing
2.5 kg?

b Elaine takes $\frac{3}{5}$ of an hour to run 5 miles. How long does it
take her to run 12.5 miles?

c A rectangle is $\frac{2}{5}$ m long and $\frac{4}{7}$ m wide. What is the area of
the rectangle? What is the perimeter of the rectangle?

1 Write these ratios in the form 1 : n.

a 3 : 9	**b** 4 : 16	**c** 5 : 10
d 7 : 21	**e** 10 : 25	**f** 15 : 60
g 4 : 28	**h** 6 : 54	**i** 22 : 33
j 18 : 24	**k** 27 : 45	**l** 36 : 48

2 Work out each of these problems.

a In a school the ratio of students to staff is 45 : 2. If there are 405 students, how many staff are there?

b In a box of chocolates the ratio of milk chocolate to plain chocolate is 5 : 4. If there are 16 plain chocolates, how many milk chocolates are there?

c A scale on a map is 1 : 250. If the distance on the map is 7 cm, what is the distance in real life?

d A model car has a scale of 1 : 20. What is the length of the model car if the real life car measures 4 metres?

3 Work out each of these problems.

a Divide £30 in the ratio 1 : 4

b Divide £120 in the ratio 5 : 7

c Divide 84 kg in the ratio 2 : 5

d Divide 135p in the ratio 8 : 7

e Divide 105p in the ratio 5 : 2

4 a A plank of wood 3.2 m long is divided into three pieces in the ratio 2 : 9 : 5. How long is each piece of wood?

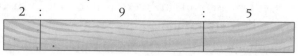

b The angles in a quadrilateral are in the ratio 1 : 2 : 4 : 5. Calculate the size of the four angles.

c The ratio of membership of men and women at a golf club is 7 : 3. If there are 660 members at the club, how many of them are women?

d Pete and Jo share £279.50 in the ratio 7 : 3. How much does Pete receive?

1 Work out each of these problems. Give your answer to 2
decimal places where appropriate.

   a Divide £38 in the ratio 1 : 5
   b Divide £1500 in the ratio 5 : 6
   c Divide 50 weeks in the ratio 2 : 5
   d Divide 600 g in the ratio 6 : 7
   e Divide 850 cm in the ratio 5 : 2

2 a Stephen, Claire and Paul buy a house together in the ratio
   4 : 3 : 2. Stephen pays £36 000. Work out the cost of the
   house.
   b Alex and Charlotte share £500 in the ratio 3 : 2.
   Alex gives a third of her share to Maneisha.
   Charlotte gives a quarter of her share to Maneisha.
   What fraction of the £500 did Maneisha receive?
   c In a shop there are a total of 120 hats and bags.
   The hats and bags are in the ratio 8 : 7.

   i Work out how many hats there are.
   ii Calculate the percentage of the 120 items that are bags.

3 Find the value of x in each of these pairs of equivalent ratios.

   a $\dfrac{5}{18} = \dfrac{x}{54}$ **b** $4 : 7 = x : 28$ **c** $\dfrac{9}{x} = \dfrac{54}{66}$

   d $7 : x = 49 : 21$ **e** $\dfrac{x}{12} = \dfrac{12}{144}$ **f** $x : 78 = 1 : 6$

4 Copy and complete the table showing four journeys.

Person	Distance travelled	Time taken	Speed
Mrs Tomes	240 miles	3.2 hours	
Ms Howard	420 km	$3\frac{1}{4}$ hours	
Mrs Flynn	38 miles	20 minutes	
Mr Collins	10 km	12 minutes	

Hint: Distance = Speed × Time

1 Recipe for Bread and Butter Pudding:

> Bread and Butter Pudding
> (for 8 people)
> 12 slices of bread
> 4 eggs
> 2 pints of milk
> 300 g raisins
> 20 g margarine

Work out the amounts needed so that there will be enough for 6 people.

2 Ravinder's father won £128.
He shared the £128 between his three children in the ratio 5 : 3 : 2.
Ravinder was given the biggest share.

a Work out how much money Ravinder received.

Ravinder saved $\frac{2}{3}$ of his share.

b Work out how much he saved.

3 Jack shares £180 between his two children Ruth and Ben.
The ratio of Ruth's share to Ben's share is 5 : 4.

a Work out how much each child is given.

Ben then gives 10% of his share to Ruth.

b Work out the percentage of the £180 that Ruth now has.

4 Triangle ABC is similar to triangle PQR.
Calculate the length of

a PQ

b AC.

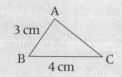
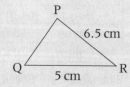

1 Work out these problems.

    a Divide £30 in the ratio 3 : 2
    b Divide £140 in the ratio 4 : 3
    c Divide 132 kg in the ratio 5 : 6
    d Divide £3.20 in the ratio 5 : 3
    e Divide £1.44 in the ratio 7 : 2

2 Write the rule for the nth term of these sequences.

    a 4, 7, 10, 13, 16, 19,..
    b 9, 13, 17, 21, 25, 29,..
    c 20, 17, 14, 11, 8, ...
    d 1, 1.5, 2, 2.5, 3, 3.5, ...

3 A cylinder of height 15 cm is shown.
The diameter of the circle is 5 cm.
Calculate

    a the area of the circle
    b the surface area of the cylinder.

4 The stem-and-leaf diagrams show the ages of people belonging to a football club and tennis club.

Football club

1	6 6 7 7 8 8 8 8 8 9 9
2	0 0 0 1 1 1 2 2 2 3 3 3 4 5 5 5 6 7 7 9 9
3	2 2 2 4 4 5 5 7 8 8 9
4	0 1 1 2 4
5	
6	

Tennis club

1	
2	3 8 8 9
3	4 4 5 5 5 6 7 7 8
4	0 0 1 1 2 2 3 3 6 7 8 8 9
5	0 0 2 2 4 5 5 6 7
6	0 0 1 4

Key: 4|1 means 41 years old

    a Calculate the median and range for both stem-and-leaf diagrams.
    b Make two comparisons between the ages of the people at both clubs.

1 This is a sketch of the plan of a room. Make an accurate scale drawing of the plan using 1 cm = 50 cm.

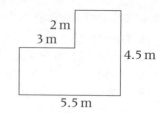

2 A map has a scale 1 : 25 000 or 1 cm represents 25 000 cm. Calculate in metres the actual distance represented on the map by

a 4 cm

b 9 cm

c 7.5 cm

d 0.25 cm

e 12.5 cm

3 Copy and enlarge each shape by the given scale factor.

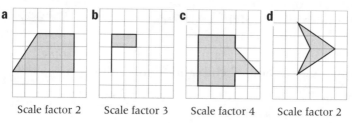

a Scale factor 2 **b** Scale factor 3 **c** Scale factor 4 **d** Scale factor 2

4 Which of the following triangles are similar to the shaded triangle? State the scale factor if the triangles are similar.

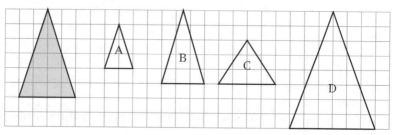

1 Copy each diagram. Find the centre of enlargement and calculate the scale factor for these enlargements. The shaded shape is the original shape.

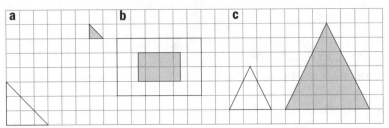

2 Copy each diagram onto squared paper.
Enlarge each shape by the given scale factor using the dot as the centre of enlargement.

a Scale factor 3

b Scale factor $\frac{1}{2}$

c Scale factor 2

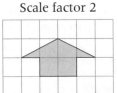

3 Calculate the unknown angle and find the two similar shapes.

A

B

C

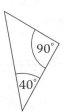

4 Calculate the value of the length marked by a letter.

a

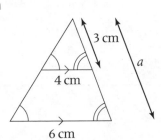

b

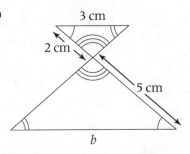

1 This shape has a perimeter of 30 cm and an area of 39 cm².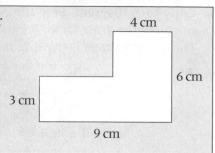

Calculate the perimeter and area of the shape after an enlargement of scale factor 3.

2 Enlarge this shape by scale factor $\frac{1}{2}$.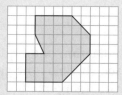

3 Copy the grid and enlarge the triangle by scale factor 2 through the centre of enlargement (0, 0).

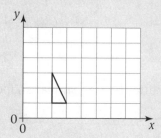

4 DE is parallel to BC

AD = 4.5 cm
AE = 6 cm
DB = 1.5 cm
DE = 3.6 cm

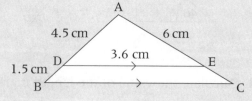

a Calculate the length of BC.
b Calculate the perimeter of the trapezium BDEC.

1 The number of minutes Sarah spends exercising each day during one week are shown in the table.

Mon	Tue	Wed	Thu	Fri	Sat	Sun
80	30	50	75	10	45	70

Draw a pie chart to represent this information.

2 Calculate the value of the unknown length.

a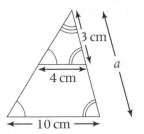

b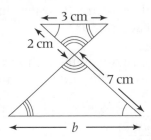

3 a Complete the table of values for $y = 4x - 3$.

x	−3	−2	−1	0	1	2	3
y							

  b On a suitable grid, draw the graph of $y = 3x - 2$.
  c Use your graph to find

    i the value of y when $x = -2.5$
    ii the value of x when $y = 3$.

4 Copy each of these calculations and insert brackets, where necessary, to make each statement correct. Not every statement needs brackets!

  a $3 + 5 \times 2 = 16$ b $8 \div 2 - 2 = 2$
  c $7 \times 3 + 9 \div 4 = 21$ d $5^2 - 5 \times 2 + 6 = 21$
  e $6 \times 3^2 - 5 = 24$ f $4 + 6 \times 9 = 58$
  g $5 + 40 \div 8 = 10$ h $3^3 + 6 \times 5 = 165$

1 Richard has a bag of sweets. He picks one sweet out at random. The probability that the sweet is a particular colour is

Colour	Red	Green	Yellow	Orange	Purple
Probability	$\frac{1}{5}$	$\frac{1}{20}$	$\frac{3}{10}$	$\frac{15}{100}$	?

a Calculate the probability of picking a sweet that is

  i purple   **ii** blue.

b If there are 40 sweets in the bag, how many of them are each colour?

2 The two-way table shows the number of students in a class who are left and right handed.

	Left-handed	Right-handed
Boy	4	12
Girl	3	9

a How many left-handed students are there in the class?

b A student is selected at random. Calculate the probability they will be

  i a boy   **ii** a left-handed girl   **iii** a right-handed boy.

3 A spinner with the numbers 10, 11, 12, 13, 14, 15, 16, 17 is spun. Calculate the probability that the spinner will land on

a an even number
b a prime number
c a multiple of 3
d a factor of 30
e a square number
f a multiple of 3 and 5
g not a prime number
h a multiple of 9
i a cube number.

1 a Decide whether each of these methods is random.

    i Selecting the first student from a register.

    ii Putting everyone's name into a hat and picking one.

    iii Selecting your closest friend.

    iv Number all students from 1–99 and roll a 0–9 dice twice to generate a 2-digit number.

  b Describe a method of random sampling that is different to any method described in part **a**.

2 Sonia wants to buy a new house. She has created a database of the six houses she is considering buying.

House	Price in £	Location	Number of bedrooms	Garden	Garage	Good condition?
1	250 000	City	3	Big	No	Yes
2	169 000	Town	3	None	No	Yes
3	213 500	Rural	2	Small	No	Yes
4	299 000	Rural	3	Big	Yes	No
5	175 000	Town	2	Big	Yes	No
6	325 000	Rural	4	Big	No	Yes

  a Which house is the cheapest with the fewest bedrooms?

  b Which house is the most expensive with 3 bedrooms?

  c Sonia wants a house in a rural location, with at least 3 bedrooms and with a big garden. She would also prefer to have a garage if possible. Which house would give her all of these things?

3 A fair dice and a spinner numbered 1–4 are thrown together.

  a List all the possible outcomes.

  b If the dice and spinner were spun 240 times how many times would you expect to get a total of 10?

4 A coin and dice are thrown together. Calculate the probability of getting

  a a Head and an even number   **b** a Head and not a 6.

  c If the coin and dice are thrown 60 times, how many times do you expect to get a Tail and a number less than 3?

1 A spinner is numbered 1 to 5.
Dale spins the spinner and throws a coin.

  a List all the possible outcomes.
  The spinner is biased.

Number	1	2	3	4	5
Probability	0.34	0.2	0.1	0.25	?

  b Work out the probability that the spinner will land on
  i 5   **ii** 6.

  c Work out the probability that the spinner will land on
  an even number.

2 22 coloured balls are used to play a game of snooker.
15 of them are red and the rest have different colours.
One of the balls is chosen at random.
Write the probability that the ball chosen will be

  a red   **b** not red.

3 A packet contains 9 green counters and 6 blue counters.
A counter is taken from the packet at random.

  a Write the probability that

  i   a green counter will be taken
  ii a yellow counter will not be taken.

  b Write all the possible outcomes of taking two counters
  from the packet.

4 A fair coin is tossed and a fair dice is thrown.

  a Copy and complete the sample space diagram to show
  all possible outcomes.

		Dice					
		1	2	3	4	5	6
Coin	Head						
	Tail			Tail, 3			

  b Calculate the probability of getting

  i a 6 and a Head   **ii** a prime number and a Tail.

1 Use a protractor and compasses to construct these sectors.

a

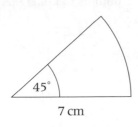

45°

7 cm

b

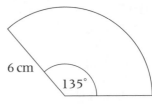

6 cm

135°

2 a To make concrete you mix sand and cement in the ratio
5 : 2. How much sand should be mixed with 20 kg of
cement?

b In a school the ratio of boys to girls is 6 : 5. If there are
1760 students in the school, how many are girls?

c A scale on a map is 1 : 250 000. If a distance on the map is
5 cm, what is the distance in real life (in metres)?

d A model car has a scale of 3 : 40. What is the length of the
model car if the real life car measures 8 metres?

3 A fair dice is rolled and a spinner is spun.
One possible outcome is (6, blue).

a Copy and complete the sample space diagram to show all
possible outcomes.

Dice

	1	2	3	4	5	6
Blue						6, blue
Red						
Green						
Yellow						

Spinner

b Calculate the probability of getting

i a 6 and a blue

ii a prime number and a red

iii a factor of 12 and a yellow

iv a square number with any colour.

1 Use the conversion graph to convert

   a 10 lb to kg
   b 6 kg to lb
   c 20 lb to kg
   d 18 kg to lb
   e 8.8 lb to kg
   f Put these weights into order starting with the lightest
     10 lb, 7 kg, 10 kg, 3 lb, 8 kg, 4.4 lb, 9 kg

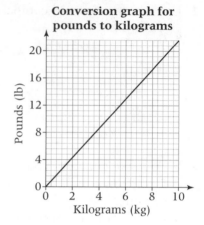

Conversion graph for pounds to kilograms

2 Find out the current exchange rate for pounds to euros.

On graph paper draw a conversion graph with pounds on the *y*-axis going up to £200.

Use your conversion graph to convert

   a £100 into euros
   b £60 into euros
   c £130 into euros
   d €160 into pounds
   e €80 into pounds
   f €300 into pounds

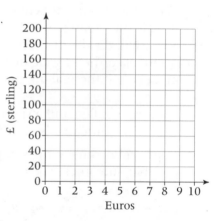

3 a Draw a conversion graph to convert between pints and litres using

     1 litre = $1\frac{3}{4}$ pints, 5 pints = $8\frac{3}{4}$ litres and 10 pints = $17\frac{1}{2}$ litres.

   b Use the conversion graph to convert

     i 6 pints to litres   **ii** 10 litres to pints
     iii 15 pints to litres   **iv** 20 litres to pints

1 Anna goes for a run to the park. This distance–time graph illustrates her journey.

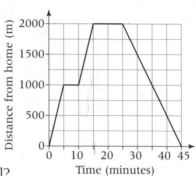

  a How long does it take her to reach the park?

  b How long does she stay at the park?

  c When was she running the slowest?

  d How far did she run in total? Convert this to miles.

2 The distance–time graph illustrates a journey.

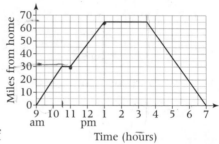

  a What happened at 10.30 am?

  b How long did they stop when they were 65 miles from home?

  c Using the conversion of 80 miles = 128 kilometres convert the total distance covered in miles to km.

3 The graph shows Teresa's journey to the shops.

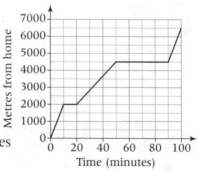

  a How many times did she stop on the way?

  b Using the formula

$$speed = \frac{distance}{time}$$

work out the speed in metres per minute between

  i   0 and 10 minutes

  ii 20 and 60 minutes

  iii 85 and 100 minutes.

1 Here is part of a travel graph of David's journey from his house to the shops and back.

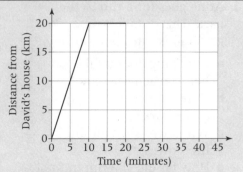

a Work out David's speed for the first 20 minutes of the journey.

David spent 10 minutes at the shops.
He then travelled back to his house at 80 km/h.

b Copy and complete the travel graph.

Hint: If Speed = $\dfrac{\text{Distance}}{\text{Time}}$, Distance = Speed × Time and Time = $\dfrac{\text{Distance}}{\text{Speed}}$.

2 Here are three containers

Water is poured into each container at a steady rate.
Match the correct graph of water height against time to its container.

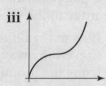

3 Sketch a graph to show the depth of water against time when these containers are filled.

S8 HW1 Review

1 Calculate these using a suitable method. Where appropriate round your answers to 2 decimal places.

   a 45% of £39   **b** 17.5% of 94 m

   c 75% of $450   **d** $\frac{8}{27}$ of 380 tonnes

   e $\frac{9}{16}$ of 85 kg   **f** 9% of 434 mm

   g $\frac{3}{4}$ of 660 km   **h** 17% of 95 m

   i 56.5% of £399   **j** Increase £219 by 14%

   k Decrease $58 by $\frac{2}{3}$ **l** Increase 19 kg by 13.5%

   m Decrease £999 by 22%   **n** Increase £699 by 17.5%

2 Copy the grid on to square grid paper. Extend the x-axis to 12 and the y-axis to 12.

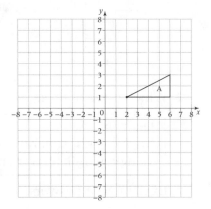

   a Reflect triangle A in the x-axis and label it B.

   b Translate triangle B by $\begin{pmatrix} 6 \\ 7 \end{pmatrix}$ and label it C.

   c Rotate triangle C through the origin (0, 0) by 90° anti-clockwise and label it D.

3 a The mean of these six numbers is 9

      6   11   10   15   9   ?

   What is the missing number?

   b The mean of these five numbers is 8 and the mode is 7.

      11   7   9   ?   ?

   What are the missing numbers?

   c The mean of these seven numbers is 9, the median is 9 and the range is 11.

      11   3   6   9   ?   ?   ?

   What are the missing numbers?

4 In the equation $3y^2 + 5y = 32$, y is a value between 2 and 3. Use the trial and improvement method to find y. Give your answer correct to one decimal place. You must show **all** your working.

1 Copy these shapes onto square grid paper. Show how each shape tessellates, using rotations and translations.

a

b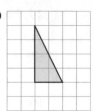

c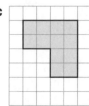

d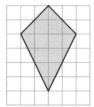

2 Which three of these regular polygons will tessellate?

Hexagon	Pentagon	Octagon
Quadrilateral (square)	Heptagon	Nonagon
Triangle (equilateral triangle)		

Explain your answers.

3 Find the value of the angles marked by letters.

a   **b** 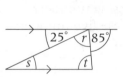   **c**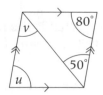

4 Use the diagram to prove that the angles of a triangle add up to 180°.

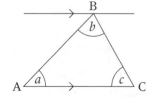

S8 HW3 Pythagoras' theorem

1 Calculate the length of the hypotenuse in these right-angled triangles. Give your answer to a suitable degree of accuracy.

a

10 cm, ?, 8 cm

b

?, 4 m, 7 m

c

6 mm, 9 mm, ?

Hint: $a^2 + b^2 = c^2$

2 Two right-angled triangles are placed together to form a triangle ACB.

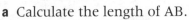

a Calculate the length of AB.
b Calculate the length of BC.
c Calculate the perimeter of triangle ABC.
d Is triangle ABC a right-angled triangle? Explain your answer.

B, 8 cm, A, 10 cm, 5 cm, C

3 Calculate the unknown length in these right-angled triangles. Give your answers to a suitable degree of accuracy.

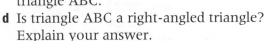

a

?, 36 mm, 25 mm

b

12 m, 5 m, ?

c

?, 11 mm, 15 mm

4 Calculate the perimeter and area of each shape.

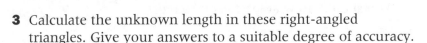

a

14 cm, 22 cm

b

12 m, 7 m, 5 m

1 a Plot and join these points
   on a copy of the grid.
   (−2, 2), (3, 2), (−3, −2),
   (2, −2)
   b What is the name of the
   shape?
   c Find the perimeter and
   area of the shape.

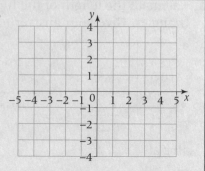

2 CD = 12 cm
  BC = 7 cm
  AB = 6 cm

   a Calculate the length of AD.
   b Calculate the area of ABCD.

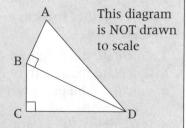

This diagram
is NOT drawn
to scale

3 On squared paper show how this shape will tessellate.
  You should draw at least eight shapes.

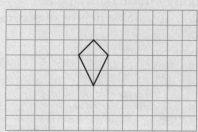

4 The diagram shows a cylinder of height
  13 cm and a radius of 5 cm.
  The length of a pencil is 14 cm.
  Show that this pencil cannot fit inside
  the cylinder.
  You cannot break the pencil.

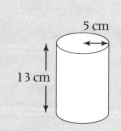

N1 HW1

1 a −1, 3   b −1, −7
   c −3, −1, 1, 3   d 0
2 a $\frac{5+8+2}{3} = 5$ b 4 and 5, 2 and 7
3 18
4 25 cm^2

S1 HW1

1 a 3004   b 45 006
   c 90 010   d 9 002 400
2 a Seven thousand five hundred
   b Two hundred and seventeen
      thousand eight hundred
   c Ninety five thousand and
      twelve
   d Seven hundred and seven
      thousand and seven
   e Nine hundred and ninety
      thousand, nine hundred and
      nine
   f Seven million, forty eight
      thousand and three
3 a 159.1   b 60.03   c 390.4
   d 48.14   e 230 100
4 a −4   b 1   c −13   d −12
   e 21   f 5   g 27   h −27
   i −48   j −49   k 0   l 36
   m −98   n 54   o −77   p 54
   q −6   r 78
5 a 8   b −1   c −7   d −15
   e −4   f 17   g −17   h −19
   i −12   j −18   k −18   l −50

A1 HW1

1 a 6.7 m   b 3000 m   c 190 cm
   d 5.3 kg   e 6.7 litres   f 9500 ml
   g 9000 kg h 14 200 g i 560 km
   j 9000 g
2 a 40 km   b 17.5 miles
   c 6 inches   d 4 kg
   e 88 km/h   f 8.7 litres
   g $\frac{2}{3}$ ft   h 1 oz
   i 0.8$\dot{3}$ pints   j 1$\frac{1}{2}$ lb

3 a 18 cm^2 b 6.25 cm
   c 9 cm   d 22.5 cm^2
4 ai 31.4 cm   aii 78.54 cm^2
   bi 21.99 cm   bii 38.48 cm^2
   ci 15.71 cm   cii 19.63 cm^2

N2 HW1

1 a $30 + 5x$ b $4x + 12$
   c $14x - 18$ d $27x + 16$
   e $7x^3 - 42$ f $5x^2 + 10x$
   g $4x^3 - 8x$ h $6x^4 + 30x^2$
   i $12x + 1$ j $16x + 12$
   k $9x$ l $12x - 15$
2 a Area = 28 cm^2
      Perimeter = 24 cm
   b Area = 40 cm^2
      Perimeter = 36 cm
3 a 1, 2, 3, 4, 6, 9, 12, 18, 36
   b 1, 2, 3, 4, 6, 8, 12, 16, 24, 48
   c 12
4 a 4 m   b 16 cm
   c 25 mm   d 8 cm

A2 HW1

1 a 6800   b 45.5   c 1560
   d 0.68   e 2600   f 59.636
   g 7 000 000   h 15.8
   i 7.000   j 15 700
   k 0.0005660   l 16.006
2 a 6700   b 280   c 552
   d 398   e 39   f 391.2
   g 1698   h 39   i 195
   j 34.385   k 446.6   l 8
3 a 650 mm b 47 m   c 6.7 kg
   d 0.6 litres e 8000 kg f 6600 m
   g 155 m   h 900 ml
4 a 72   b −32   c 156
   d 2   e 16   f −7

D1 HW1

1 a $b = 3$ b $f = 6$ c $f = 3$
   d $p = 36$ e $m = 6$ f $r = 32$
   g $d = 9$ h $r = 10$ i $k = 2.5$
   j $t = -6$ k $f = 30$ l $p = -11$

2 a 3005 **b** 22 404 **c** 11 022
  d 1 000 100 **e** 999 099
3 a Sixty seven thousand
  b Forty thousand and seven
  c Six hundred and eighty seven thousand nine hundred
  d Eleven million
  e Four million six hundred thousand and seven
  f Six hundred and ninety nine thousand nine hundred and ninety nine
4 a 2.8 cm **b** 7.16 mm
  c 7 cm **d** 6 m
5 a 85 **b** 160 **c** 24 **d** 6
  e 320 **f** 20 **g** 10 **h** 140
  i 90 **j** 20

N3 HW1

1 a

Speed, mph	Frequency
35–39	1
40–49	2
50–59	4
60–69	7
70–79	8
80–89	5

b 3

2 ai 55 **aii** 32
  bi $\frac{9}{119}$ **bii** $\frac{55}{119}$
3 a 10 km, 10 miles, 55 000 ft
  b 35 mph, 60 km/h, 45 mph
  c 12 inches, 29 cm, 1.2 ft
  d 400 ml, 4 pints, 4 litres
4 a $x > 2$
  b $x < \frac{1}{2}$
  c $x \leqslant -3$
  d $x \leqslant 4$
  e $x \geqslant 8\frac{1}{2}$
  f $x < -\frac{1}{2}$

S2 HW1

1 a $\frac{3}{8}$ **b** $\frac{3}{10}$ **c** $\frac{1}{6}$ **d** $\frac{1}{2}$ **e** $\frac{9}{10}$
  f $\frac{7}{9}$ **g** $\frac{31}{20}$ **h** $\frac{5}{21}$ **i** $\frac{33}{35}$
2 a 0.011, 0.099, 0.646, 0.9, 0.98
  b $\frac{1}{5}, \frac{3}{8}, \frac{3}{4}, \frac{7}{9}, \frac{6}{7}$
  c 0.45, $\frac{4}{7}$, 65%, $\frac{2}{3}, \frac{7}{9}$
3 $\frac{2}{5}$, 0.4, 40%; $\frac{3}{4}$, 0.75, 75%; $\frac{1}{4}$,
  0.25, 25%; $\frac{2}{3}$, 0.$\dot{6}$, 66.$\dot{6}$%;
  $\frac{1}{8}$, 0.125, 12.5%; $\frac{3}{10}$, 0.3, 30%;
  $\frac{1}{100}$, 0.01, 1%; $\frac{1}{200}$, 0.005, 0.5%;
  $\frac{1}{12}$, 0.08$\dot{3}$, 8.$\dot{3}$%; $\frac{13}{20}$, 0.65, 65%.
4 a b^5 **b** t^2 **c** m^5 **d** t^9 **e** n^7 **f** p

A3 HW1

1 a $a = 25°$ **b** $b = 85°$
  c $c = 65°$ **d** $d = 105°$ **e** $e = 105°$
  d $f = 25°$ **e** $g = 129°$
  f $h = 9°$ **i** $i = 85.5°$
2 ai $2x + 4 = 14$ **aii** $x = 5$
  bi $\frac{x}{4} + 6 = 11$ **bii** $x = 20$
  ci $6x - 8 = -10$ **cii** $x = -\frac{1}{3}$
3 What sports do you like?: too much scope in reply. Better to ask 'Which of the following sports do you play regularly?'
  Don't you think that exercise is good for you?: the question is weighted – it presupposes a positive response. Better to ask 'How many times per week do you exercise?'
4 a $\frac{1}{4} > \frac{1}{5}$ **b** $\frac{9}{10} > \frac{9}{12}$ **c** $\frac{7}{10} < \frac{4}{5}$
  d $\frac{4}{5} > \frac{19}{25}$ **e** $\frac{5}{12} > \frac{1}{4}$ **f** $\frac{29}{100} < \frac{3}{10}$

D2 HW1

1 a Acute **b** Reflex **c** Reflex
  d Acute **e** Reflex
2 ai 11, 13, 15 **aii** $2n + 1$
  bi 23, 20, 17 **bii** $38 - 3n$
  ci 37, 43, 49 **cii** $6n + 1$
  di $-10, -14, -18$ **dii** $14 - 4n$
  ei $-2, 1, 4$ **eii** $3n - 17$

3 a

Height, h, cm	Tally	Frequency
$5 < h \leqslant 10$	⊞ I	6
$10 < h \leqslant 15$	⊞ IIII	9
$15 < h \leqslant 20$	⊞ I	6
$20 < h \leqslant 25$	⊞ ⊞ I	11
$25 < h \leqslant 30$	⊞ II	7

b 24   **c** $20 < h \leqslant 25$

4 a $\frac{2}{15}$ **b** $\frac{1}{7}$ **c** $\frac{18}{25}$ **d** $\frac{7}{19}$ **e** $\frac{5}{28}$

   f $\frac{5}{18}$ **g** $\frac{10}{9}$ **h** $\frac{18}{35}$ **i** $\frac{25}{48}$ **j** $\frac{6}{5}$

   k $\frac{36}{5}$ **l** $\frac{7}{5}$

A4 HW1

1 a $36°$ **b** $144°$

2 a $7x + y$ **b** $8x + y$ **c** $3x - 3y$

   d $-10x - 3y + 6z$ **e** $4x$

   f $11x - 10y$ **g** 0 **h** $9x + 2y + z$

3 a 10   **b** $4°$

c

Film	Angle(°)
Thriller	52
Comedey	116
Horror	20
Science Fiction	84
Romance	48
Action	40

d

Action 10   Thriller 13   Romance 12   Science ficition 21   Horror 5   Comedy 29

4 a

Weight (kg) vs Height (cm)

b As height increases, weight increases also.

c Positive correlation.

D3 HW1

1 a $4n - 1$ **b** $2n + 4$ **c** $3n + 9$

   d $13 + 6n$ **e** $11 - n$

2 a $\frac{6}{5}$ **b** $\frac{3}{2}$ **c** $\frac{3}{4}$ **d** $\frac{12}{10}$ **e** $\frac{3}{2}$

   f $\frac{15}{14}$ **g** $\frac{49}{30}$ **h** $\frac{19}{21}$ **i** $\frac{51}{60}$

3 a

x	0	1	2	3	4	5
y	3	5	7	9	11	13

b, c

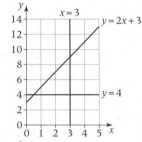

di $x = \frac{1}{2}$ **dii** $x = 0$

4 a 5 km, 6000 m, 5 miles

   b 1.5 kg, 1700 g, 1 tonne

   c 20 inches, 1 metre, 6 feet

   d 10 cm, 1000 mm, 1 m

   e 100 oz, 10 lb, 10 kg

N4 HW1

1 a $\frac{2}{9}$ **b** $\frac{1}{3}$ **c** $\frac{4}{9}$

2 a

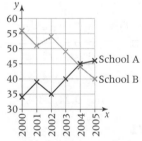

b School A percentages have increased, whilst school B percentages have decreased.

c School A overtook School B.

3 a $76°$ **b** $40°$

4 a $3x + 12$ **b** $4x^2 + 20x$

   c $2x^2 - 10x$ **d** $5x^3$

S3 HW1

1

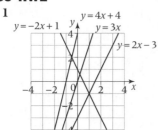

$y = -2x + 1$ $y = 4x + 4$ $y = 3x$ $y = 2x - 3$

2 a 24 cm^2 **b** 40 mm^2
  c 16 cm^2 **d** 30 m^2
  e 28.27 cm^2 **f** 19.63 cm^2

3 a 60 mph **b** 66.67 mph
  c 80 mph **d** 100 mph

4 a 0.15 **b** 30

N5 HW1

1 a €14 **b** €21 **c** €168 **d** €700
  e £4 **f** £110 **g** £120 **h** £160

2

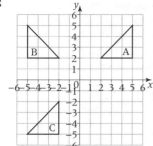

  c Reflect A in line $y = -x$

3 a 0.1 **b** 0.6

4 a 0.29, 0.3, $\frac{1}{3}$, 35%, $\frac{3}{5}$

  b $\frac{3}{7}$, 0.6, 60%, 0.62, $\frac{2}{3}$

  c $\frac{1}{24}$, $\frac{1}{12}$, 0.12, 0.24, 24%

A5 HW1

1 a 1, 3, 5, 9
  b 1, 4, 9, 16, 49, 100, 144
  c 1, 8, 216, 1000
  d 1, 2, 3, 6; 9 **e** 2, 3 **f** 9 **g** 24

2 a i and **ii** **b ii** and **iii**

3 a $x = 5$ **b** $x = 2$ **c** $x = -2$
  d $x = 20$ **e** $x = -6$ **f** $x = -4$
  g $x = -2$ **h** $x = 6$

4

4	9
5	2 3 7 7 7 9 9
6	0 9
7	0 2 2 3 4 5 6 7 9
8	0 1 3 3 8 9
9	0 1 6 9 Key: 6|0 = 60 kg

S4 HW1

1 a 36 **b** 196 **c** 64 **d** 1
  e 225 **f** 36 **g** 343 **h** 1728
  i 1000 **j** 9 **k** 13 **l** 4
  m 26 **n** 70 **o** 10

2 a $3x + 15$ **b** $4x - 16$ **c** $x^2 + 4x$
  d $4x + 10$ **e** $-3x - 9$ **f** $-2x^2 + 8x$
  g $7x - 4$ **h** $9x - 24$ **i** $12x + 11$

3 a △ **b** ▱ **c**

4

N6 HW1

1 a ＋ **b** ◇

  Cube   Square-based pyramid

2 a $a = 12 - 3b$ **b** $a = \frac{15 + 3b}{2}$
  c $a = 24 - 8b$ **d** $a = 5b + 25$
  e $a = \frac{15 - 6b}{3}$

3 a 1 : 4 **b** 1 : 3 **c** 1 : 4
  d 1 : 2 **e** 1 : 5 **f** 1 : 3
  g 1 : 8 **h** 1 : 6 **i** 1 : 2
  j 1 : 1.5 **k** 1 : 1.5 **l** 1 : 1.5

4 a 150 g **b** 900 g **c** 2250 g

5 a £775 **b** £1550 **c** £2325

6 a 65 kg **b** 45 kg **c** 125 kg

A6 HW1

1 a Area = 28.27 cm^2
    Perimeter = 18.85 cm
  b Area = 15 cm^2
    Perimeter = 16.2 cm

c Area = 24 cm^2
Perimeter = 22 cm
d Area = 47 cm^2
Perimeter = 44 cm

2 a 50 **b** 15 **c** 26 **d** 96

3 a 15x cm^2 **b** $x = 9$ cm
c 30 + 2x **d** $x = 24$ cm

4 a

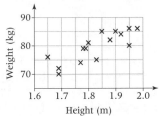

b As height increases, there is a slight increase in weight.
c Positive correlation

D4 HW1

1 a Trapezium **b** Prism
c Kite **d** Cylinder
e Cuboid **f** Pyramid
g Parallelogram **h** Parallelogram
i Cube **j** Triangle

2 b **d** **e**

f **i**

3 a 425 **b** 384 **c** 15 615
d 53 **e** 56 **f** 13
g 45.6 **h** 127.5 **i** 67.32
j 12.5 **k** 5.3 **l** 3.25

4 a $\frac{1}{5}$ **b** $\frac{3}{10}$ **c** $\frac{1}{2}$ **d** 0 **e** 40

S5 HW1

1 a **c**

2 £1216.67

3 a 23 cm **b** 12 cm
c 7 and 8, since $7^2 = 49$ and $8^2 = 64$

4 a 59 **b** 11 **c** 3 **d** 5 **e** 2.5 **f** 4.5

N7 HW1

1 5.5

2 a

Number of goals	Frequency
0	7
1	6
2	7
3	8
4	9
5	2

b Mean = 2.5 Median = 2.5
Mode = 9 Range = 5

3 a **b**

4 a 10 **b** 9
c The girls' median mark was higher, but their range was larger, whilst the boys had a lower median but less spread in the marks.

D5 HW1

1 a 95° **b** 96° **c** 271° **d** 310°
2 a £275 **b** £300 **c** £49.50
d 60.6p **e** €345 **f** $208
g 28p **h** $238.80
3 3, 5, 5, 7
4 a 46 **b** 23 **c** 108 **d** 39

S6 HW1

2 ai £104 **aii** £112
bi £82.40 **bii** £87.42
3 a $5x + 6 = 36$ $x = 6$
b $9 - x = -3$ $x = 12$
c $27 = 4x + 3$ $x = 6$
4 a

20	2
21	4
22	2 7
23	4
24	5 6 6 7
25	5 6 7
26	0 3 5 7 7 7
27	6 8 8 8 9
28	1 7 7
29	0 1 8 8 9

b 267 secs

Key: 24|6 = 246 secs

A7 HW1

1 a Volume = 90 cm^3
Surface Area = 126 cm^2
b Volume = 47.25 cm^3
Surface Area = 79.5 cm^2
c Volume = 6 cm^3
Surface Area = 20.8 cm^2

2 a 90° **b** 50° **c** 2.5°
di 36 **dii** 20 **diii** 32 **div** 56

3 a 46.5 **b** 67.95 **c** 356.459
d 14.0 **e** 34.57 **f** 14.00

4 a 600 mm^2 **b** 9 cm^2
c 0.06 m^2 **d** 100 000 cm^2
e 9 km^2 **f** 6 000 000 m^2

N8 HW1

1 a 28 m^3 **b** 50 cm^3

2 d, e, c, f, h, b, a, g

3 One would expect $\frac{120}{6}$ = 20 sixes, so the die may not be fair.

4 a 22.5 kg **b** 1.5 hrs
c Area = $\frac{8}{35}$ m^2 Perimeter = $\frac{68}{35}$ m

S7 HW1

1 a £18 : £12 **b** £80 : £60
c 60 kg : 72 kg **d** £2 : £1.20
e £1.12 : £0.32

2 a $3n + 1$ **b** $4n + 5$
c $23 - 3n$ **d** $\frac{n+1}{2}$

3 a 19.63 cm^2 **b** 274.89 cm^2

4 a Football club:
Median = 24.5   Range = 28
Tennis club:
Median = 43   Range = 41
b Tennis club attracts older members.
Tennis club has larger age range.

D6 HW1

1

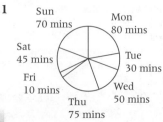

Sun 70 mins
Mon 80 mins
Sat 45 mins
Tue 30 mins
Fri 10 mins
Wed 50 mins
Thu 75 mins

2 a a = 7.5 cm **b** b = 10.5 cm

3 a

x	−3	−2	−1	0	1	2	3
y	−15	−11	−7	−3	1	5	9

b

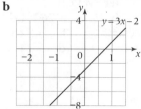

$y = 3x - 2$

ci $y = -13$ **cii** $x = 1.5$

4 a $(3 + 5) \times 2 = 16$ **b** $(8 \div 2) - 2 = 2$
c $7 \times (3 + 9) \div 4 = 21$ **d** $5^2 - (5 \times 2) + 6 = 21$
e $6 \times (3^2 - 5) = 24$ **f** $4 + (6 \times 9) = 58$
g $5 + (40 \div 8) = 10$ **h** $(3^3 + 6) \times 5 = 165$

A8 HW1

1 Answers may vary.

2 a 50 kg **b** 800
c 12 500 m **d** 60 cm

3 a

	1	2	3	4	5	6
Blue	1 B	2 B	3 B	4 B	5 B	6 B
Red	1 R	2 R	3 R	4 R	5 R	6 R
Green	1 G	2 G	3 G	4 G	5 G	6 G
Yellow	1 Y	2 Y	3 Y	4 Y	5 Y	6 Y

bi $\frac{1}{24}$ **bii** $\frac{1}{8}$ **biii** $\frac{5}{24}$ **biv** $\frac{1}{3}$

S8 HW1

1 a £17.55 **b** 16.45 m
c $337.50 **d** 112.59 tonnes
e 47.81 kg **f** 39.06 mm
g 495 km **h** 16.15 m
i £225.44 **j** £249.66
k $19.33 **l** 21.57 kg
m £779.22 **n** £821.33

2

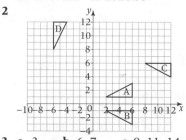

3 a 3 **b** 6, 7 **c** 9, 11, 14

4 $y = 2.5$